THIN TWIN
RECIPE BOOK

SLIMMING
MAGAZINE

ARGUS BOOKS

THIN TWIN

EDITOR: Sybil Greatbatch
RECIPES DEVISED BY: Sarah Johnson
and Glynis McGuinness
DESIGN: Carolyne Sibley

First published by Argus Books 1991

Argus Books,
Argus House
Boundary Way
Hemel Hempstead
Herts HP2 7ST
England

ISBN 1 85486 057 7

Printed and bound in Great Britain by Clays Ltd., St Ives
plc, Bungay

THIN
TWIN

CONTENTS

INTRODUCTION

f you want to get slim and stay that way you need to exchange some old habits for new ones. So toss out all those old cookery books and base your eating on Thin Twin recipes. Not only are Thin Twins lower in calories than traditional recipes, they are healthily lower in fat, too. So you can be sure that when you switch to Thin Twin cooking your whole family is bound to benefit. And the great thing is that they probably won't even notice that the delicious meal you serve up is helping your figure, too.

All the recipes in this book have been tested by Slimming's experts to make sure they are no less delicious than their "fat twin' classic dishes. You will get a similar size portion, too. But a Thin Twin costs about half the calories of a traditional recipe, and can easily be incorporated into any diet or maintenance plan.

It's been proved over and over again that the diet that is going to succeed for you is the one that includes the foods you enjoy eating and which fits into your usual lifestyle. If you never normally have breakfast, for example, there is no need to force yourself to eat early in the day because this meal is listed on a diet menu. Keep those calories for later in the day when you do feel hungry.

There is absolutely no need to feel deprived when you are dieting and once you have mastered the Thin Twin technique you can say goodbye to excess pounds for ever. Just make it a habit to look hard at each old favourite recipe you enjoy, then create its Thin Twin. Thin Twins still taste good, still look lovely, but they're much lower in calories.

Spot the Thin Twin. You get a scrumptious 150g/5oz helping of strawberries for 35 calories. But top them with 45ml/3 level tablespoons double cream and your dessert costs 200 calories. The dessert on the right is topped with creamy-tasting fromage frais which adds just 45 calories to the strawberries and means your dessert totals just 80 calories.

DO YOU NEED TO LOSE WEIGHT?

Check the chart on the following page. Make sure that you know your correct height, too, as the right weight for you is governed by this. Because there is no such thing as a precise ideal weight you should use these charts as a general guide only. As you near the target weight that you have set yourself, take a critical look at your figure in front of a full-length mirror. If you can't see any ugly bulges and if you can no longer grab handfuls of fat in problem places, then you have achieved your ideal weight.

If you are dieting, try to weigh yourself once a week on the same scales, at the same time of day, wearing similar clothes. Most people weigh lightest first thing in the morning and hourly fluctuations in body weight can mislead you about your slimming progress.

HOW DO YOU DO IT?

If you want to get healthily slim and stay that way, there's really just one all important secret. All effective slimming diets depend for their success on a single basic formula. You must bring the total calories you take in each day to a level below what you are burning up. Then your body has to call on its fat reserves to make up the deficit.

The lowest you ever need to go to lose weight is 1,000 calories if you are a woman or 1,250 calories if you are a man. The heavier you weigh the more calories your body needs to function, which is why *Slimming*'s experts always recommend that a woman who has over 3st to lose should start dieting on 1,500

calories and cut down to 1,250 calories when she has less than 3st surplus to go. Men, again, can add a daily 250 calories to these figures. It should only be necessary to go down as low as 1,000 calories a day when you near target or if your weight loss seems to slow down. You can average these intake figures, if you wish, over several days or a week. For instance, if you are planning to spend extra calories on a special meal for a Saturday evening you can eat fewer calories on Friday and Sunday to balance this out.

KEEP HEALTHY

Calories aren't your only consideration, of course. You must see that your diet includes all the nutrients you need. A good basic rule of nutrition is to choose from as wide a range of foods as possible.

Follow the modern good-health guidelines which call for a diet high in carbohydrate with most of your calories coming from vegetables, cereals, pulses, seeds and nuts. Fat, particularly saturated fat, should be kept to a minimum and meals should be low in sugar, have less salt and be high in fibre.

PLANNING YOUR DIETING MENUS

Calorie counting remains the classic slimming method. It has the great advantage of flexibility. Within a sensible framework you can eat quite literally anything you like and still lose weight, provided you do not exceed your overall calorie allowance for each day or for each week.

When you are planning your menus for the day, start with the most important meal. Then decide on how many calories that leaves you to spend on other meals or snacks during the day. There are calorie charts for all basic foods at the back of this book.

Before you begin a diet it is best to get out a pencil and paper and work out what you are going to eat for at least the next few days, the next week if possible. Try to buy as many of your meal ingredients as possible in one shopping trip. That keeps confrontation with tempting foods that are not on your list to a minimum. However, don't keep fresh vegetables hanging around the kitchen for long as their vitamin value will gradually deteriorate.

STAYING THERE

A major part of staying slim is to put into practice some of the new good habits you have learned while you were slimming. If you simply go back to your old ways of eating, then the chances are that you will just put those pounds right back on again. The Thin Twin recipes in this book can help you to maintain your weight when you incorporate them into your regular meal repertoire. Here's some other stay in shape tips.

KEEP BUSY

Boredom is probably one of the main reasons that people nibble mindlessly on food that they really are not hungry for. So consciously seek out new interests, pastimes or even a new job. Now that you know you can be successful at losing weight you should have the confidence to know that if you really set your mind at doing something else you could succeed just as well at that, too.

A GUIDE TO YOUR IDEAL WEIGHT

Heights are minus footwear; but these ideal-average weights include an allowance of 2 to 3lb (about 1kg) for light indoor clothing.

THESE CHARTS PROVIDE no more than an educated guide to your ideal weight: your proper poundage could be around 10lb or so either side of the figure given for your height. Seeing you in the flesh, though, an expert could probably estimate very closely the weight at which you'd be likely to feel and look your best.

FORGET ABOUT "BIG BONES" and wrist, hand or shoe measurements as an indication of whether you should weigh more or less. Consider instead your skeleton's spread. Neat and narrow body "scaffolding" will call for less cladding than would a rangier bone structure. You're aiming at a flesh layer that looks good and feels non-flabby.

IF SEVERAL STONES TOO HEAVY, be prepared to readjust your ideal weight once you near your target. For instance, many a long-time "big girl" discovers that her flab had been concealing a smaller frame than she'd imagined. Or - less likely - somebody may appear a bit bony at her original "ideal" and look better at a target 4 or 5lb higher.

IF YOU ARE A WOMAN			
4-ft-10	1.47m	7-st-7	47.5kg
4-ft-11	1.50m	7-st-9	48.5kg
5-ft-0	1.52m	7-st-12	50kg
5-ft-1	1.55m	8-st-1	51.5kg
5-ft-2	1.57m	8-st-4	52.5kg
5-ft-3	1.60m	8-st-7	54kg
5-ft-4	1.63m	8-st-11	56kg
5-ft-5	1.65m	9-st-0	57kg
5-ft-6	1.68m	9-st-5	59.5kg
5-ft-7	1.70m	9-st-9	61kg
5-ft-8	1.73m	9-st-13	63kg
5-ft-9	1.75m	10-st-3	65kg
5-ft-10	1.78m	10-st-7	66.5kg
5-ft-11	1.80m	10-st-11	68.5kg
6-ft-0	1.83m	11-st-1	70.5kg
IF YOU ARE A MAN			
5-ft-2	1.57m	9-st-0	57kg
5-ft-3	1.60m	9-st-4	59kg
5-ft-4	1.63m	9-st-7	60.5kg
5-ft-5	1.65m	9-st-10	61.5kg
5-ft-6	1.68m	9-st-13	63kg
5-ft-7	1.70m	10-st-3	65kg
5-ft-8	1.73m	10-st-8	67kg
5-ft-9	1.75m	10-st-12	69kg
5-ft-10	1.78m	11-st-2	71kg
5-ft-11	1.80m	11-st-7	73kg
6-ft-0	1.83m	11-st-11	75kg
6-ft-1	1.85m	12-st-1	76.5kg
6-ft-2	1.88m	12-st-6	79kg
6-ft-3	1.90m	12-st-11	81kg
6-ft-4	1.93m	13-st-2	83.5kg

THIN TWIN

KEEP ACTIVE

Exercise has all sorts of benefits apart from burning up extra calories. It can help you to relax, make you feel good, help tone up flab so that you look good, too. You may have decided to take up some form of exercise to help you lose weight, so don't just give it up when you get there. Or if you felt too fat to get into a leotard before you slimmed, now there is no excuse and stretching and toning exercises may be just what those under-used muscles need to make you even trimmer. Try to work some exercise into your regular rou-tine so that it doesn't become a chore. Even an extra brisk walk for 30 minutes a day can have benefits for both health and fitness and staying slim power.

BUY SLIM-FITS

Include some slim fitting clothes into your new wardrobe. A snug waistband or belt will sharply remind you if any pounds start going on again. Then you can take immediate action. Give away or throw out all those oversize outfits that you'll never want to wear again. Not being able to get into a favourite outfit or

A mixed salad adds up to very few calories - 25 in this bowlful. Serve with 45ml/3 level tablespoons ordinary French dressing, though, and the calories per serving will shoot up to 250. Partner the salad with the same amount of oil-free French dressing and it becomes a Thin Twin at just 30 calories.

being unable to find anything to comfortably wear for that special occasion is a great incentive to slim off excess pounds.

BAN RESTRICTIVE THINKING

Don't dwell on the items you have had to cut down. Instead think of all the delicious new taste experiences that a concern for your weight has given you. To stay in shape you must create a healthier new normal way of eating. You need to make permanent changes so that you know that you never need to go back to being fat ever again. The healthy diet you've chosen to follow, if you take the advice given in this book, will make meals more enjoyable, not less. Good eating.

STARTERS
AND
LIGHT MEALS

Some of the recipes in this chapter are ideal as starters when you are entertaining. All could be served as a light meal – either on their own or accompanied by extras such as a bread roll, salad or crispbreads.

A bowl of soup or a dip with vegetable crudités could be a diet-saving snack, too.

Home-made soup is nothing like anything you'll get from a packet or can. No bought soup will compare for flavour and filling power. And don't even consider buying a ready-prepared dip for raw vegetables. They are usually based on oil or mayonnaise and are bound to be very high in calories.

You will find all these recipes just as flavoursome as their far higher calorie counterparts and you certainly won't miss out on quantity.

You may not usually bother with a starter unless you are making a special meal for family or friends. But a low-calorie first course can have advantages for a slimmer. If you tend to eat rather quickly, you could consume quite a lot of food before your stomach has had time to pass on the signal that hunger has been satisfied. That is why you may polish off a main course and still feel as if you could eat lots more. But wait for about 20 minutes and that feeling will usually go away. If you go on to eat more, you could end up feeling that you've eaten far too much. If you have a starter, then give yourself a little rest before going on to the main course, you may well find that you won't want to cram down every calorie in sight. If you don't want to bother with a starter try eating an apple about 20 minutes before your meal – it will do the same trick.

Light meals can be accompanied by lots of salad vegetables. Pile up your plate with shredded lettuce, sliced cucumber, shredded carrots and cabbage. As long as you don't add a high calorie dressing, your salad will probably not cost more than about 30 calories. If a dressing makes a salad go down extra easily, then select one of the many low-calorie dressings that are now available. Serve a salad with ordinary French dressing and 45ml/3 level tablespoons will add up to 225 calories. Partner the salad with the same amount of oil-free French dressing and the total cost will be 5 calories. Although low-calorie alternatives to salad cream and

mayonnaise are not as cheap calorie-wise as oil-free French dressing, they are still well worth using. A reduced-calorie salad dressing is 25 calories for a level 15ml tablespoon compared to 55 for ordinary salad cream. Reduced-calorie mayonnaise is around 45 calories for a level 15ml tablespoon compared to 110 calories for a real mayonnaise.

The recipes in this chapter serve from one to six people, but are mainly for four. Soups are always worth making in bulk and can be frozen in individual portions for re-heating as required. Portions of pâtés and dips can be kept in the refrigerator for a couple of days. If you wish to make the recipes serve a smaller number of people, just cut down the quantities accordingly.

AVOCADO MOUSSE

10g sachet gelatine

½ chicken stock cube

225ml/8floz water

1 medium ripe avocado

30ml/2 tablespoons lemon juice

10ml/2 teaspoons Worcestershire sauce

75g/3oz fromage frais, 0% fat

75ml/3 level tablespoons reduced-calorie mayonnaise

Salt and pepper

Lemon

Sprinkle the gelatine over 150ml/5floz water in small bowl and dissolve by standing bowl over pan containing hot water. Mix stock cube with remaining water and stir into gelatine. Set to one side to cool. Halve the avocados and remove stones. Scoop out flesh with a fork and mash with lemon juice until smooth or purée in a liquidizer or food processor. Season with salt and pepper and Worcestershire sauce. Pour gelatine mixture into avocado mixture and stir to mix thoroughly. Fold in fromage frais and mayonnaise. Pour into a dampened 575ml/1 pint mould or 4 individual dishes and chill until firm. Serve in individual dishes or by turning out from mould.

A MEDIUM AVOCADO weighing approximately 115g/ 4oz will cost 250 calories, which makes it rather costly for a fruit. This recipe used one avocado between four people and makes a delicious starter which all avocado lovers will enjoy.

INSTEAD OF the traditional home-made fatty stock, we used half a chicken stock cube mixed with water which saved us around 75 calories.

THE BIGGEST SAVING of all comes from substituting virtually fat-free fromage frais for double cream. Double cream costs 375 calories for 75g/3oz, while the fromage frais which is labelled 0% fat costs 45 calories (the 8% fat fromage frais with added cream would be 50 calories more). The saving here, then, is a massive 330 calories.

MAYONNAISE, TOO, will make any recipe's calories soar. In place of the standard sort costing 120 calories per 15ml level tablespoon, we used a reduced-calorie mayonnaise costing 45 calories for the same amount. That saved a total 225 calories.

THIS MOUSSE is far lower in fat than a traditional recipe, but is still creamy-tasting – light and lovely enough to eat on its own. Alternatively you could serve the mousse with crispy Melba Toast or warmed mini pitta breads.

TRADITIONAL RECIPE
Serves 4 at 340 calories per portion

THIN TWIN
Serves 4 at 125 calories per portion

COLESLAW

Serves 4/115 calories per portion

450g/1lb white cabbage

175g/6oz carrots, peeled weight

2 sticks celery

75g/3oz onion

25g/1oz sultanas

75ml/5 level tablespoons reduced-calorie mayonnaise

30ml/2 level tablespoons fromage frais, 8% fat

Salt and pepper

Shred the cabbage and grate carrots. Slice the celery and finely chop onion. Place vegetables in a large bowl with the sultanas. Mix together the mayonnaise and fromage frais and season to taste. Stir into the vegetables and chill before serving.

Because it is usually made with ordinary mayonnaise, a traditional coleslaw can be much higher calorie than it looks. In fact, crunchy salad could very easily amount to 270 calories a serving.

POTATO SALAD

Serves 4/160 calories per portion

450g/1lb new potatoes

8 spring onions

90ml/6 level tablespoons reduced-calorie mayonnaise

30ml/2 level tablespoons fromage frais, 8% fat

30ml/2 level tablespoons chopped chives

Salt and pepper

Place the potatoes in cold water. Bring to the boil and cook for 15-20 minutes, until just tender. Drain and leave until cold. Slice the potatoes and finely chop the onion and place in salad bowl. Mix the mayonnaise and fromage frais together and sprinkle in the chives. Add to the potatoes and onion and mix well. Chill before serving.

A traditional recipe for potato salad would be around 335 calories for a serving. Again it's the mayonnaise that does the damage. We mixed reduced-calorie mayonnaise with fromage frais for a much lower calorie, but still tasty, dressing.

CURRIED CHICKEN LIVERS

Serves 2/215 calories per serving

115g/4oz onion

75g/3oz yellow pepper

225g/8oz chicken livers

5ml/1 teaspoon oil

1 clove garlic

5ml/1 level teaspoon curry powder

Salt and pepper

30ml/2 level tablespoons fromage frais, 8% fat

10ml/2 teaspoons chopped parsley

Finely chop the onion, cut pepper into strips and chop the livers. Heat the oil in a non-stick pan and add the onion and crushed garlic and cook for 2 minutes, until soft. Stir in curry powder and cook for 1 minute. Add the peppers and livers and cook, stirring frequently, for 3-4 minutes. Season with salt and pepper to taste. Stir in the fromage frais. Sprinkle with parsley and serve.

A traditional recipe calls for much more oil to be used to fry the vegetables. And you could end up with a dish costing 435 calories. Serve these Curried Chicken Livers as a light meal with crispbreads.

THOUSAND ISLAND DIP

Serves 4/65 calories per serving

30ml/2 level tablespoons low-calorie salad dressing

175g/6oz fromage frais, 8% fat

60ml/4 level tablespoons tomato ketchup

10ml/2 level teaspoons creamed horseradish

45ml/3 level tablespoons low-fat natural yogurt

Dash Tabasco

Salt and freshly ground black pepper

Put salad dressing in a bowl with fromage frais, tomato ketchup and creamed horseradish. Mix well and add yogurt and Tabasco. Season to taste with salt and freshly ground black pepper. Divide into portions and chill before serving. A portion of this dip can be served with vegetable crudités. A 115g/4oz mix of carrot, celery and cucumber sticks would add about 20 calories.

Whether you make a Thousand Island Dip to a traditional recipe, or buy it ready prepared, it is unlikely to add up to under 200 calories for a serving. Here we cut calories by using low-calorie salad dressing, fromage frais and low-fat natural yogurt.

BLUE CHEESE DIP

150g/5oz low-fat soft cheese with garlic & herbs

90ml/6 level tablespoons fromage frais, 0% fat

25g/1oz Danish Blue cheese

15ml/1 level tablespoon chopped chives

450g/1lb vegetables (carrots, peppers, celery, baby corn, baby courgettes and cherry tomatoes)

Put the soft cheese, fromage frais, Danish Blue cheese and chives into a liquidizer or food processor and blend until smooth. Cut carrots, peppers, celery into sticks. Arrange vegetables in a dish and serve with dip.

BLUE STILTON which costs 117 calories per 28g/1oz is one of the highest calories cheeses you can use. And a traditional recipe for Blue Cheese Dip would use at least 150g/5oz, adding up to a tremendous 585 calories. We've based our dip on low-fat soft cheese at just 44 calories per 28g/1oz and added 25g/1oz Danish Blue at 98 calories per ounce to give it that distinctive blue cheese flavour.

THE LOW-FAT CHEESE is flavoured with garlic and herbs, which means that there is no need to add crushed garlic – no great calorie saving, but more convenient.

A TRADITIONAL RECIPE would normally use about 150ml/5floz soured cream (290 calories) to give the dip its creamy texture. The low-fat cheese is already blended and it just needs the addition of 90ml/6 level tablespoons fromage frais, 0% fat, totalling 90 calories to make the texture nicely light.

YOU CAN SERVE any mix of crudités that you like with the dip. Ideal are carrots, peppers, celery and cucumber cut into batons. Whole baby corn, baby courgettes, cherry tomatoes, baby leeks and spring onions are delicious, too. If you are very strictly counting calories you should allow an extra 25 calories for 115g/4oz mix of all these vegetables.

TRADITIONAL RECIPE
Serves 4 at 220 calories per portion

THIN TWIN
Serves 4 at 100 calories per portion

PRAWN BISQUE

Serves 4/125 calories per portion

75g/3oz onion
1 chicken stock cube
275ml/½ pint boiling water
275ml/½ pint skimmed milk
225g/8oz prawns
60ml/4 level tablespoons tomato purée
60ml/4 level tablespoons fromage frais, 0% fat
1.25ml/¼ teaspoon paprika
30ml/2 tablespoons dry sherry
15ml/1 tablespoon chopped chives
Salt and ground black pepper

Finely chop onion and mix stock cube with the water to make the stock. Set aside a few prawns for garnish and put the remainder in a food processor or liquidizer with the tomato purée, stock, milk and onion. Blend until smooth and pour into a pan. Stir until just below boiling point. Add the fromage frais, paprika, sherry and salt and pepper and cook over a low heat for 2-3 minutes more. Serve in bowls, garnished with prawns and chives.

A luxurious soup which could cost you 125 calories a portion more – a traditional recipe would cost 250 calories. We used fromage frais instead of cream, and a stock cube instead of more fatty stock – the result is just as delicious.

CARROT AND ORANGE SOUP

Serves 6/85 calories per portion

175g/6oz onion
1½lb carrots, peeled weight
1 chicken stock cube
275ml/½ pint skimmed milk
Salt and pepper
1 medium orange
15ml/1 tablespoon oil
850ml/1½ pints boiling water

Finely chop onion and slice carrots. Mix the stock cube with water. Heat the oil in a non-stick pan and add the onion and cook for 4-5 minutes until softened. Add the carrots, stock, milk and seasoning and bring to the boil. Reduce heat, cover and simmer for 30 minutes or until the carrots are tender. Cool slightly then blend soup in liquidizer or food processor. Squeeze juice from the orange and grate the rind. Add the orange rind to the soup with the juice. Reheat the soup gently, then adjust seasoning if necessary.

A delicious low-calorie soup ideal for a starter, but the traditional version would cost at least 180 calories a serving. Calories have been cut by using less oil to fry the vegetables and skimmed milk instead of whole milk and cream.

SMOKED FISH CHOWDER

Serves 6/155 calories per portion

450g/1lb smoked haddock fillet
850ml/1½ pints water
150ml/¼ pint skimmed milk
2 medium onions
15ml/1 level tablespoon plain flour
225g/8oz potatoes, peeled weight
150g/5oz carrots, peeled weight
10ml/2 teaspoons oil
1 fish stock cube
150ml/5floz fromage frais, 0% fat
Salt and pepper

Place the haddock in a pan with 150ml/5floz water and simmer for 10 minutes or until tender. Drain and flake the fish, discarding any bones. Finely chop onion and slice potatoes and carrots. Heat the oil in a non-stick pan and sauté the onions until soft. Stir in the flour and cook for a further minute. Mix fish stock cube with 725ml/1¼ pints water, the skimmed milk and add to pan. Bring to the boil, stirring until thickened. Add potatoes and carrots and season to taste. Then simmer for 10 minutes until tender. Stir in haddock and blend until smooth. Stir in fromage frais and heat until warm. Adjust seasonings if necessary.

Calories are cut by using the minimum of oil for frying the onion, reducing the amount of flour used for thickening and by adding fromage frais instead of cream. A traditional fish chowder would cost about 280 calories a portion.

VICHYSOISSE

Serves 4/150 calories per portion

275g/10oz leeks, trimmed weight
450g/1lb potatoes, peeled weight
1 medium onion
850ml/1½ pints boiling water
1 chicken stock cube
Freshly grated nutmeg
Salt and pepper
25g/1oz skimmed milk powder
30ml/2 level tablespoons fromage frais, 0% fat
Fresh chives

Slice the leeks and dice the potato. Finely chop the onion. Place vegetables in pan with water, stock cube, nutmeg and seasoning. Bring to the boil and simmer for 25-30 minutes until vegetables are tender. Blend the milk powder with 45ml/3 level tablespoons water and stir into soup with 150ml/¼ pint extra water. Either chill or reheat. To serve, swirl fromage frais into each bowl of soup and sprinkle with chives.

Traditionally all the vegetables in this tasty soup are fried in a lot of butter. In our Thin Twin version we don't fry at all. We also cut out double cream and use skimmed milk powder, with a swirl of fromage frais to serve. The saving is around 230 calories a portion

CREAM OF WATERCRESS SOUP

175g/6oz watercress

1 medium onion

725ml/1¼ pints water

2 chicken stock cubes

Salt and pepper

60ml/4 level tablespoons skimmed milk powder

10ml/2 level teaspoons cornflour

90ml/6 level tablespoons fromage frais, 0% fat

Wash watercress and discard any hard stalks. Chop onion and place in pan with 575ml/1 pint water and the crumbled stock cubes. Season with salt and pepper. Bring to the boil, cover and simmer for 10 minutes. Add watercress and simmer for another 10 minutes. Cool slightly, then purée the soup in a liquidizer or food processor. Blend the skimmed milk powder with the cornflour and remaining water. Add to the soup and return to the pan. Bring to boil, stirring all the time, until soup thickens. Then simmer for 2 to 3 minutes. Stir in fromage frais and serve.

THE WATERCRESS IS usually sautéed with 50g/2oz butter in a traditional recipe for cream of watercress soup. In this Thin Twin the watercress is cooked in stock, which brings out its flavour nicely while saving 420 butter calories.

TO THICKEN a traditional soup, flour is mixed into the butter-fried watercress before any liquid is added. Here instead of 25g/1oz flour, we used 10ml/2 level teaspoons cornflour mixed with water which thickened the soup sufficiently and saved just over 20 calories.

IF YOU USE A STOCK which is home-made it's hard to know how many calories it will contain. That's because any fat marbled into meat or fish will melt into the broth. Even if you skim off any fat that floats to the top, some is likely to remain – but exactly how much would be hard to determine from one stock to another. If you use stock cubes, calories are controlled. The two we used in this recipe add up to a maximum 60 calories (some makes will cost less).

INSTEAD OF A FULL PINT of whole milk which is usually blended with stock to make the cream soup, we added 60ml/4 tablespoons skimmed milk powder saving 310 calories. It helps to thicken the soup, gives it a creamy taste and contributes to the soup's lovely pale green colour.

TRADITIONAL RECIPE
Serves 4 at 305 calories per portion

THIN TWIN
Serves 4 at 65 calories per portion

MUSHROOM SOUP

Serves 6/85 calories per portion

115g/4oz onion

275g/10oz mushrooms

225g/8oz potatoes, peeled weight

10ml/2 teaspoons oil

1 vegetable stock cube

575ml/1 pint water

275ml/½ pint skimmed milk

Salt and pepper

2.5ml/½ teaspoon nutmeg

30ml/2 level tablespoons fromage frais,
8% fat

Chopped parsley

Chop onion, slice mushrooms and dice potato. Heat oil in a non-stick pan and sauté onion and mushroom for 2-3 minutes. Mix stock cube with water and add to pan with milk, potato and seasonings. Bring to boil, cover and simmer for 10-15 minutes. Blend in a food processor or liquidizer until smooth. Return to pan and heat thoroughly. Serve with a swirl of fromage frais and parsley.

We've used more very-low-calorie mushrooms, fewer higher calorie potatoes, less oil and swapped whole milk for skimmed. Then we added a swirl of fromage frais instead of cream. Result — a tasty soup for just 85 calories a portion, compared to 200 calories for the traditional version.

LETTUCE SOUP

Serves 4/70 calories per serving

350g/12oz lettuce

8 spring onions

25g/1oz low-fat spread

15ml/1 level tablespoon plain flour

1 chicken stock cube

575ml/1 pint boiling water

150ml/¼ pint skimmed milk

Salt and pepper

Roughly shred the lettuce and finely chop the onions. Heat the low-fat spread in a non-stick pan and add the lettuce and spring onions and cook until soft. Stir in the flour. Mix the stock cube with the water and add to the pan. Bring to the boil; cover and simmer for 20 minutes. Allow the soup to cool slightly, then purée in a liquidizer or food processor until smooth. Return soup to the pan and add milk and seasoning. Reheat gently.

Low-fat spread (we used a brand suitable for cooking) is used instead of butter and skimmed milk instead of cream to make this unusual soup. A traditional version would be at least 175 calories a serving.

FRENCH ONION SOUP

Serves 4/150 calories per serving

4 medium onions

10ml/2 teaspoons oil

2 chicken stock cubes

1.15 litres/2 pints water

225ml/8floz dry white wine

Salt and freshly ground black pepper

50g/2oz Gruyere cheese

Cut onions into fine rings, then halve them. Heat oil in a non-stick pan and sauté the onions for 5 minutes until soft, stirring occasionally. Mix the stock cubes and water together and add to the onions with wine and seasonings. Bring to the boil and simmer for 15-20 minutes until onions are cooked. Divide grated Gruyere cheese between four serving dishes and pour soup on top.

French onion soup often looks a lot more innocent than it actually is. That's because when onions are fried in lots of oil they can gain an enormous number of calories. A fatty stock will add to the soup's total, too. You could pay up to 280 calories a serving for this starter.

SWEETCORN AND CRAB SOUP

Serves 4/150 calories per serving

298g/10½oz can sweetcorn

4 spring onions

575ml/1 pint water

275ml/½ pint skimmed milk

2 chicken stock cubes

15ml/1 tablespoon soy sauce

30ml/2 tablespoons dry sherry

30ml/2 level tablespoons cornflour

75g/3oz white crab meat, canned

Salt and pepper

Reserving 2 tablespoons place the sweetcorn and the liquid from the can in a liquidizer or food processor and blend until smooth. Finely chop onions and put in a saucepan with the sweetcorn, water, milk, stock cubes and soy sauce. Bring to the boil and simmer for 10 minutes. Mix the sherry with cornflour until smooth and add to the soup. Cook for 1-2 minutes, stirring all the time. Add the flaked crab meat to the soup with reserved sweetcorn. Heat through and season. Serve hot.

Serve a portion of this tasty soup as a starter, or a larger helping as a light meal with a piece of French bread. Calories are much lower than the 300 per serving of a traditional recipe.

BAKED CRAB

75g/3oz onion

250g/9oz crab meat, white or brown

10ml/2 teaspoons oil

75g/3oz wholemeal breadcrumbs

10ml/2 level teaspoons French mustard

Cayenne pepper

Salt

115g/4oz fromage frais, 0% fat

25g/1oz Edam cheese, grated

Finely chop onion. Flake crab meat, taking care to remove any membranes or shell particles. Heat the oil in a non-stick pan and cook onion until softened. Add crab meat, 50g/2oz breadcrumbs, mustard and season with pepper and salt to taste. Cook for 2 to 3 minutes. Stir in fromage frais and adjust seasonings. Spoon into ramekins or scallop shells. Sprinkle with Edam cheese mixed with remaining breadcrumbs. Bake at 170˚C/ 325˚F, gas mark 3 for 20-25 minutes.

THE TRADITIONAL recipe asks you first to take 50g/2oz butter (420 calories) in which you fry the onion and mix with crab meat. We used a minimum 10ml/2 teaspoons oil (80 calories) and saved 340 calories.

WE INCREASED the amount of crab we used in our Thin Twin recipe. At 36 calories per 25g/1oz, crab costs less than breadcrumbs (61 calories for wholemeal). So we reduced the breadcrumbs by 25g/1oz and increased the crab meat by the same amount – saving 25 calories.

AT 125 CALORIES for just 25g/1oz , double cream is a very high calorie addition to any recipe. In a traditional baked crab recipe you would usually use at least 115g/4oz double cream mixed with 50g/2oz Greek-style yogurt – total 565 calories. In our Thin Twin version we used 115g/ 4oz fromage frais which still gives a creamy taste, but saves 505 calories.

BEFORE BAKING the crab mixture is usually topped with Cheddar cheese. Instead of 50g/2oz Cheddar (234 calories) we used 25g/1oz Edam (90 calories) mixed with 25g/1oz breadcrumbs. This saved an additional 85 calories, while giving our tasty starter a crispy, cheesy topping.

TRADITIONAL RECIPE
Serves 4 at 380 calories per portion

THIN TWIN
Serves 4 at 195 calories per portion

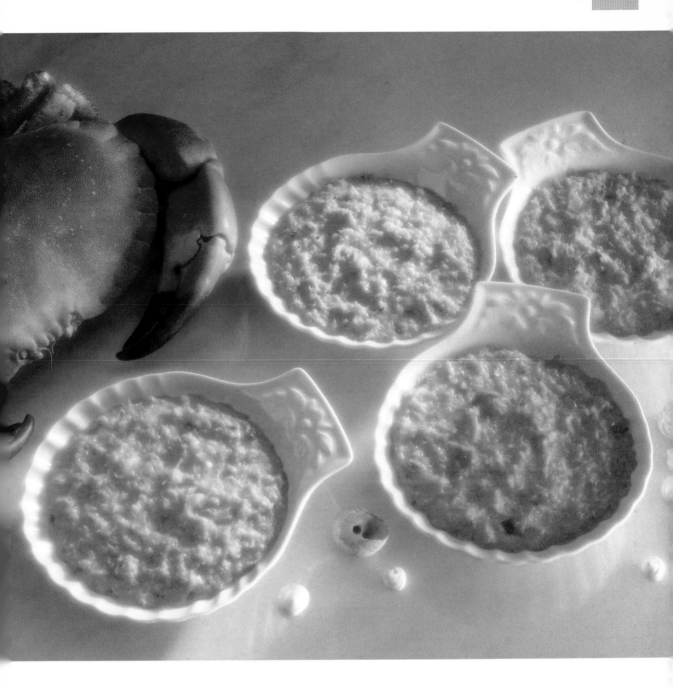

CURRIED PARSNIP SOUP

Serves 6/120 calories per portion

150g/5oz onion

700g/1½lb parsnips, peeled weight

10ml/2 teaspoons oil

5ml/1 level teaspoon curry powder

2.5ml/½ level teaspoon ground cumin

1 chicken stock cube

850ml/1½ pints boiling water

275ml/½ pint skimmed milk

Salt and pepper

75ml/5 level tablespoons fromage frais, 8% fat

Paprika to garnish

Finely chop onion and dice parsnip. Mix stock cube with the water. Heat the oil in a non-stick pan and add onion and cook for 4 to 5 minutes. Add the parsnips, curry powder and cumin and cook for a further 2 minutes. Add stock, milk and seasoning, then bring to the boil. Reduce heat, cover and simmer for 40 minutes until vegetables are tender. Allow to cool slightly then blend in a liquidizer or food processor until smooth. Return purée to the pan and adjust seasoning. Add the fromage frais and reheat gently, but do not boil. Sprinkle with a little paprika before serving.

> A winter warming soup which would normally cost you around 250 calories a serving. This Thin Twin cuts calories by using the minimum of oil to fry the vegetables and by using fromage frais instead of cream.

FISH SCALLOPS

Serves 4/240 calories per portion

115g/4oz mushrooms

225g/8oz cooked smoked haddock, skin and bones removed

450g/1lb potatoes, peeled weight

10ml/2 level teaspoons low-fat spread

5ml/1 teaspoon oil

275ml/½ pint skimmed milk

30ml/2 level tablespoons cornflour

2.5ml/½ level teaspoon English mustard

Salt and freshly ground black pepper

15g/½oz reduced-fat Cheddar cheese

25g/1oz wholemeal breadcrumbs

Slice mushrooms and flake the haddock. Boil potatoes, drain and mash with 30ml/2 tablespoons milk and low-fat spread. Keep warm. Heat the oil in a non-stick pan and sauté mushrooms for 2-3 minutes. Blend the cornflour with a little milk to form a smooth paste and place the remainder in a pan. Bring to the boil and pour over blended milk. Return to heat and stir until thickened. Season and add mustard, mushrooms and haddock. Divide the mixture between 4 scallop shells and sprinkle with cheese and breadcrumbs. Pipe the potato around the edge of each dish. Bake at 200°C/400°F, gas mark 6, for 15-20 minutes until topping is crisp.

> We've used skimmed milk instead of cream, reduced-fat Cheddar cheese instead of ordinary Cheddar. The potato topping is mashed with skimmed milk and low-fat spread instead of butter. Result: a saving of 225 calories a portion.

PRAWN COCKTAIL

Serves 4/175 calories per portion

90ml/6 level tablespoons tomato ketchup

90ml/6 level tablespoons low-calorie
salad dressing

30ml/2 level tablespoons reduced-calorie
mayonnaise

60ml/4 level tablespoons fromage frais,
0% fat

5ml/1 level teaspoon creamed
horseradish

Few drops Tabasco

275g/10oz prawns, fresh or defrosted

Lettuce, shredded

Freshly ground black pepper

Mix the tomato ketchup, salad dressing, mayonnaise and fromage frais together. Add the horseradish and Tabasco. Season with pepper. Place
lettuce in 4 serving dishes. Add prawns and pour
over the dressing. Chill before serving.

**Low-calorie salad dressing,
reduced-calorie mayonnaise and fromage
frais instead of cream, mean that this
popular starter is 175 calories a portion
instead of 390 calories.**

TUNA PÂTÉ

Serves 4/130 calories per serving

198g can tuna in brine

60ml/4 level tablespoons reduced-calorie
mayonnaise

60ml/4 level tablespoons fromage frais,
8% fat

45ml/3 tablespoons dry sherry

Salt and freshly ground black pepper

Drain tuna and flake roughly. Mix the mayonnaise,
fromage frais and sherry together. Add to the tuna
and season. Chill well before serving.

**An easy to make, but delicious fish pâté
that you could serve either as a starter or
with crispbreads as a light meal. A
traditional recipe which uses cream and
mayonnaise would be around 300
calories the same size portion.**

COUNTRY PÂTÉ

115g/4oz fillet of pork

225g/8oz pig's liver

1 medium onion

1 clove garlic

15ml/1 level tablespoon tomato purée

Black pepper

2.5ml/½ level teaspoon mixed herbs

1.25ml/¼ level teaspoon grated nutmeg

1 egg, size 3

Discard any fat and gristle from the pork. Finely chop in a food processor (or mince) with liver and onion. Add the crushed garlic, tomato purée, seasonings and the egg. Mix well, then spoon into a 450g/1lb loaf tin lined with foil. Cover and place in a baking dish containing a little water. Cook at 180°C/ 350°F, gas mark 4, for 1 hour. Leave to cool, then cover surface of the pâté with foil. Chill in the refrigerator. Garnish with chopped or sliced red pepper (optional).

A PÂTÉ TRADITIONALLY often used up the fatty cuts of meat and lots more fat was added during cooking. For our Thin Twin we used very lean pork fillet and just made sure that any visible fat that remained was trimmed away. Pork fillet is 35 calories an ounce compared to 76 calories for fatty leg of pork or 180 calories an ounce for belly pork.

THERE IS NOT A LOT of difference in the calories of liver. But you will save almost 60 calories by using pig's liver instead of lamb's in this recipe. The pig's liver with its stronger flavour is a good pâté ingredient, too.

THE ONION IS NORMALLY pre-fried in oil. We found that if you chopped the onion with the meat in a food processor, this really wasn't necessary. And this saved 120 calories.

REMEMBER THAT WHEN you grease a loaf tin your pâté will absorb the calories of the fat during cooking and these would need to be added into the total. We lined the tin with foil instead. A traditional pâté also often has melted butter spread on top and this could add an extra 420 calories.

TRADITIONAL RECIPE
Serves 4 at 280 calories per portion

THIN TWIN
Serves 4 at 160 calories per portion

MUSHROOM PÂTÉ

Serves 4/100 calories per portion

225g/8oz mushrooms

50g/2oz onion

50g/2oz low-fat spread

2.5ml/½ level teaspoon dried mixed herbs

30ml/2 tablespoons dry sherry

Salt and pepper

115g/4oz skimmed milk soft cheese

Chopped parsley

Finely the chop mushrooms and onions. Melt the low-fat spread in a non-stick pan and add the mushrooms, onions and herbs and cook over a low heat, stirring frequently until onion is soft. Add sherry and continue to cook until all the liquid is evaporated. Season to taste. Blend until smooth. Leave to cool. Mix with the cheese and chill. Sprinkle with parsley before serving.

Mushrooms for a pâté are usually fried in lots of butter – we used low-fat spread suitable for cooking. The fried mushrooms would then be mixed with cream cheese – we used skimmed milk soft cheese. Made the traditional way a portion of mushroom pâté would cost about 240 calories.

CHICKEN LIVER PÂTÉ

Serves 6/160 calories per portion

450g/1lb chicken livers

50g/2oz lean ham

115g/4oz onion

15ml/1 tablespoon oil

1-2 cloves garlic, crushed

75ml/5 level tablespoons fromage frais, 0% fat

50g/2oz skimmed milk soft cheese

15ml/1 level tablespoon tomato purée

30ml/2 level tablespoon dry white wine

Salt and pepper

Chopped parsley

Clean chicken livers and dry with absorbent paper. Dice ham and finely chop the onion. Heat oil in a non-stick pan and sauté onion and garlic for 2-3 minutes until softened. Add the livers and cook for a further 4-5 minutes until browned. Cool slightly, then add fromage frais, soft cheese, tomato purée, wine, ham and seasonings. Place in a liquidizer or food processor and blend until smooth. Transfer to a serving dish and chill before serving.

Lean ham is used instead of streaky bacon, and a tablespoon of oil is used for cooking the livers instead of about 50g/2oz butter. Fromage frais gives a creamy texture without the high calorie cost of cream and dry white wine is used instead of the traditional brandy. No butter is poured on top before chilling, either. Result: a delicious pâté that costs 160 calories instead of 320 a portion.

SMOKED SALMON PÂTÉ

Serves 4/140 calories per serving

175g/6oz smoked salmon

150g/5oz skimmed milk soft cheese

25ml/5 teaspoons lemon juice

60ml/4 level tablespoons fromage frais, 8% fat

15ml/1 level tablespoon freshly chopped dill

Freshly ground black pepper

Roughly cut the salmon and place in a liquidizer or food processor with the skimmed milk soft cheese, fromage frais and lemon juice. Blend until smooth. Add the dill and season with black pepper. Spoon into individual dishes. Chill before serving.

Using skimmed milk soft cheese instead of cream cheese and fromage frais instead of cream, not only cuts calories from the 300 a portion a traditional recipe would normally cost it also means this luxurious pâté has a lighter texture and stronger salmon flavour.

CHICKEN AND HAM MOUSSE

Serves 4/160 calories per serving

175g/6oz cooked lean chicken

50g/2oz lean smoked ham

30ml/2 tablespoons lemon juice

75ml/5 level tablespoons reduced-calorie mayonnaise

60ml/4 level tablespoons fromage frais, 8% fat

30ml/2 tablespoons dry sherry

Salt and pepper

Fresh coriander and lemon zest to garnish

Finely chop the chicken and smoked ham and mix together. Stir in the lemon juice, mayonnaise, fromage frais, sherry and seasoning. Mix thoroughly and spoon into individual ramekins and chill. Garnish with coriander and lemon zest.

Serve this mousse with a warmed pitta bread and salad. Makes a tasty lunch for just 245 calories. A traditional mousse on its own would cost more than that. If the mousse was made with cream and mayonnaise calories would go up to about 330 a portion.

THIN
TWIN

CORONATION CHICKEN

50g/2oz onion

10ml/2 level teaspoons curry powder

2.5ml/½ teaspoon lemon juice

15ml/1 level tablespoon tomato purée

¼ chicken stock cube

125ml/4floz water

25g/1oz apricot chutney

150g/5oz reduced-calorie mayonnaise

1 small carton low-fat set natural yogurt

450g/1lb cooked chicken, no skin or bones

Chop onion. Place in a small pan with curry powder, lemon juice, tomato purée, stock cube and water. Bring to the boil; cover and simmer for 8 minutes. Cool. Mix apricot chutney into the curry mixture, then liquidize until smooth. Stir in mayonnaise and yogurt. Cut chicken into bite-sized pieces. Pour sauce over to coat the chicken.

TO BRING THE CALORIE count tumbling down, we've used reduced-calorie mayonnaise in place of the ordinary sort: that means a saving of around 100 calories for every ounce added.

BETTER STILL, we've only added half the usual amount of mayonnaise and used a carton of low-fat natural yogurt (75 calories) in place of 150g/5oz ordinary mayonnaise (1,025 calories), making a tremendous saving of 950 calories!

THE TRADITIONAL recipe calls for poaching a whole chicken and then using the fatty stock to make the sauce.

We've added flavour by using ¼ chicken stock cube at a cost of 9 calories.

WHY USE jam when you can use a chutney? You'll save more precious calories by making this simple swap, because apricot chutney has less sugar than apricot jam – but, importantly, the sauce tastes just as good.

FOR THE FINAL crowning glory we've kept an excellent flavour but cut some other traditional high-calorie ingredients (no sugar, no wine and definitely no whipped cream), to make Coronation Chicken a Thin Twin recipe to always treasure.

TRADITIONAL RECIPE
Serves 4 at 875 calories per portion

THIN TWIN
Serves 4 at 320 calories per portion

Daily Mail, Thursday, May 14, 1998

I WAS accosted in my local pub by two men: did I know what a caper was?

It was a question in an inter-pub quiz and the answer given had been: pickled nasturtium seeds.

In fact, that is incorrect — although in the past nasturtium seeds pickled with vinegar and spices were used as an alternative when capers were unavailable.

Pickled broom buds often served the same purpose in the 16th and 17th centuries. But capers are the unopened young flower buds of a prickly low-growing shrub, *Capparis spinosa*, native to the Mediterranean region.

The berries are also pickled with herbs and used as a smart condiment with cold meats.

Capers have been popular here since the 15th century, when they were imported by the barrel-load from Europe. Eliza Acton has a simple recipe (in Modern Cookery For Private Families, 1845) for caper sauce to accompany boiled mutton or fish, in which chopped-up capers are added to hot melted butter with a dash of vinegar.

Look out for salted capers which, to my mind, are superior to the sharper vinegared variety.

CELIA'S RECIPE OF THE DAY

COD WITH CAPER SAUCE

INGREDIENTS
(SERVES 4)

150-200g (5-7oz) cod fillet per person

Olive oil for frying

For the sauce:

2 shallots or 1 small onion, chopped

1tbsp butter

3-4tbsp dry white wine

450ml (15fl oz) fish stock

150ml (5fl oz) double cream

2tbsp capers

50g (2oz) baby spinach, optional

To serve:

2 each carrots and leeks, julienned and lightly steamed

■ HAVE you a favourite recipe you'd like to share with other Daily Mail readers? Send it to Celia Goodrick-Clarke, Recipe Of The Day, Northcliffe House, 2 Derry Street, London W8 5TT.

METHOD

TO MAKE sauce, soften shallot in butter until shiny. Add wine and boil fast to reduce by two-thirds. Add stock and cream and reduce by one-third. Add roughly-chopped capers, boil for one minute and test seasoning. If liked, add spinach with capers, boil one minute to wilt, then whiz in blender to make smooth green sauce. Meanwhile, divide cod into equal pieces, season and pan-fry on both sides for two minutes — depending on thickness — in a little hot oil. Serve fish on a bed of vegetables with caper sauce poured over.

Daily Mail, Thursday, May 14, 1998

Moore like poe

QUESTION The famous poem The Funeral Of Sir John Moore tells how his troops buried him in an unmarked grave at dead of night after the Battle of Corunna in 1809. Has his grave ever been located and marked?

THE Battle of Corunna, on January 16, 1809, was part of the Peninsula War in which Britain sought to deny the Napoleonic French the use of the Iberian peninsula.

Sir John Moore, executing a fighting retreat, held off a far greater French army of 42,000 under Marshal Soult, and successfully evacuated most of his 24,000 men but was hit by grapeshot and died later that evening.

The poem first appeared anonymously in 1817 but was written by the Irish poet Charles Wolfe (1791-1823). Its most famous stanzas go:

Not a drum was heard, not a
funeral note,
As his corse to the rampart we

SALAD NIÇOISE

Serves 4/205 calories per portion

225g/8oz French beans

225g/8oz new potatoes

2 eggs, size 3

175g/6oz cucumber

4 medium tomatoes

8 black olives

50g/2oz anchovy fillets, drained

198g/7oz can tuna in brine, drained

Lettuce, shredded

75ml/5 tablespoons oil-free French dressing

Boil beans and potatoes; then drain and cool. Dice the potatoes. Hard-boil the eggs, then slice. Slice the cucumber and tomatoes and halve the olives. Break tuna into bite-sized chunks and divide the anchovy fillets into strips. Place the shredded lettuce in the base of a serving dish. Add the prepared salad ingredients. Pour over the dressing and toss well. Chill before serving.

Salad is not necessarily a low-calorie starter choice. This traditional favourite could cost 375 calories a portion. Calories are cut mainly by using oil-free French dressing instead of the oily sort. And by using tuna in brine, rather than tuna canned in oil. Eat this salad as a light meal, too, accompanied with crispbreads.

WALDORF SALAD

Serves 4/165 calories per portion

3 medium eating apples

Juice ½ lemon

2 sticks celery

25g/1oz walnuts

75ml/5 level tablespoons reduced-calorie mayonnaise

30ml/2 level tablespoons fromage frais, 8% fat

40g/1½oz raisins or sultanas

Freshly ground black pepper

Lettuce, shredded

Core apples, then slice and toss in lemon juice. Roughly chop the celery and walnuts. Combine the mayonnaise and fromage frais. Add apple, celery, walnuts and raisins then mix well. Season to taste. Place the lettuce in a dish. Spoon in the Waldorf Salad and chill before serving.

This crunchy salad is low enough in calories to serve as a snack, but the traditional version would have cost you 340 calories a portion. Calories are cut by using reduced-calorie mayonnaise and fromage frais instead of cream. We've also cut the amount of walnuts used as these add up to 149 calories for 25g/1oz.

CHEESE OMELET

Serves 1/280 calories

2 eggs, size 3

15ml/1 tablespoon water

Salt and freshly ground black pepper

25g/1oz reduced-fat Cheddar cheese

10ml/2 level teaspoons low-fat spread

1 medium tomato

Lightly beat eggs and water together. Season with salt and pepper. Grate the cheese. Melt the low-fat spread in a non-stick pan and brush over the surface. Make the omelette by pouring in the egg mixture and cooking for 1½-2 minutes. Sprinkle over the cheese. Add the sliced tomato and fold over. Serve immediately with green salad.

Made with whole milk, ordinary Cheddar cheese and butter this light omelet could add up to 510 calories. We used water instead of milk, reduced-fat Cheddar and low-fat spread. We reduced the amount of cheese we used, too, and bulked up the filling with a sliced tomato. If you wish you could sprinkle on some herbs for no extra calorie cost.

CAULIFLOWER CHEESE

Serves 2/305 calories per serving

450g/1lb cauliflower florets

2 medium tomatoes

30ml/2 level tablespoons cornflour

275ml/½ pint skimmed milk

70g/2½oz matured Cheddar cheese

Salt and pepper

5ml/1 level teaspoon French mustard

45ml/3 level tablespoons fresh wholemeal breadcrumbs

Boil the cauliflower for about 15 minutes or until tender. Slice the tomatoes. Meanwhile blend cornflour with a little milk until smooth. Heat the remaining milk, then pour onto the cornflour, stirring. Return to the pan and bring to the boil, stirring all the time. Simmer for 1-2 minutes. Grate the cheese and add to the sauce reserving 2 tablespoons. Season with salt, pepper and mustard. Drain cauliflower and place in an ovenproof dish with the sliced tomatoes. Pour over the sauce. Sprinkle over remaining cheese and breadcrumbs. Grill until the topping browns.

You could use a reduced-fat cheese for this sauce if you wish, but we have used an ordinary Cheddar. But, because we chose the highly-flavoured matured sort, we have added far less to the sauce than a traditional recipe requires. The sauce calories still come down to half those of a traditional serving. The sauce is made with cornflour instead of a roux of flour and butter which reduces calories, too.

KEDGEREE

225g/8oz smoked haddock

175g/6oz long-grain brown rice

1 large onion

15ml/1 level tablespoon curry paste

575ml/1 pint water

Salt and pepper

2 eggs, size 4

60ml/4 tablespoons half cream

Coriander or parsley, fresh

Poach fish in a little water until cooked. Keep warm. Meanwhile put rice, chopped onion and curry paste in a saucepan with 575ml/1 pint water. Season to taste with salt and pepper and bring to the boil. Cover and simmer for 30-40 minutes or until rice is cooked. Drain off any remaining water. Hard-boil the eggs, then shell and cut into slices. Flake fish and stir into rice mixture, then add cream and mix together. Spoon into serving dish with sliced eggs and coriander or chopped parsley.

FIRST WE HALVED the amount of fish that is usually recommended and for extra bulk added a large onion. This swap saved around 25 calories a portion.

USING BROWN RICE instead of white only saves a few calories, but it also adds a little more fibre to the dish.

THE MAIN CALORIE COST in any traditional kedgeree recipe is the butter or margarine into which the other ingredients are stirred. The recommended amount can be as much as 75g/3oz, and by cutting this out entirely we saved about 630 calories (160 per portion).

RECIPES NOT LAVISH with butter tend to have rather more cream added. By using half cream instead of single cream you save 10 calories per tablespoon.

CURRY IS AN OPTIONAL ingredient so you can leave it out if you wish. You won't save many calories worth counting, though.

THERE IS 20 CALORIES difference between a large size-1 egg and the size-4 we use. When you are trimming recipes' calories, these little amounts can add up to big total differences.

SERVED UP ON ITS OWN or with a little green salad, Thin Twin Kedgeree makes a delicious low-calorie meal.

TRADITIONAL RECIPE
Serves 4 at 455 calories per portion

THIN TWIN
Serves 4 at 285 calories per portion

MAIN
MEALS

Whether you are looking for a family meal which is quick and easy to prepare or something a little more special, you will find a Thin Twin recipe here. Each recipe has been carefully trimmed of calories while keeping it just as tasty and satisfying as its traditional counterpart.

Some of the dishes can be served without an accompaniment, but if you wish to add vegetables or perhaps rice, pasta or bread, then consult the calorie charts at the back of the book.

You can easily add extra bulk to a meal without adding many extra calories if you pile your plate with vegetables. But remember that if you add any butter or margarine to boiled vegetables or oily dressings to salads you can add an enormous number of calories. In fact,

when you change to the low-fat Thin Twin way of eating, you will find that you will actually prefer vegetables unadorned. When you are cooking vegetables you can either boil them, steam them or microwave them without adding to their calorie cost. Instead of frying mushrooms or courgettes, put them in a pan with a little stock made with a stock cube and cook quickly until the stock evaporates. Then dry-fry the vegetables in the pan until slightly browned. If you get yourself a good quality non-stick frying pan you will be able to stir-fry vegetables in a tiny amount of oil. At 120 calories for a tablespoon, oil is one of the highest calorie ingredients you can add to a dish. Depending on the amount of vegetables you are frying, it is possible to use just one teaspoon of oil to start off the vegetables, for as soon as their juices start to run there will be enough moisture in the pan. Start off with the vegetables that need the longest cooking time, such as carrots and add the quick-to-fry vegetables last.

If you are cooking meals just for yourself, choose ones that can be frozen and divide into individual portions. You could freeze portions of lasagne, spaghetti sauces on their own, cooking the pasta when you are ready to serve up the meal. Casseroles and curries will freeze too.

After you have chosen the Thin Twin meal you intend to cook, make out a shopping list for all the ingredients. When cooking Thin Twins it is not a good idea to start improvising and making ingredient substitutions if you don't have exactly the right items in your storecupboard. The recipes have been carefully tested to give you a really good flavour, and calories could be altered by substitutions, too.

Incorporate these Thin Twin main meals into your daily menus on a regular basis and getting slim and staying that way will be so much easier.

LASAGNE

350g/12oz extra-lean ground beef

115g/4oz lean gammon

1 medium onion

4 sticks celery

115g/4oz mushrooms

1 green pepper

400g/14oz can tomatoes

1 stock cube

2 cloves garlic

2.5ml/½ level teaspoon mixed herbs

2.5ml/½ level teaspoon oregano

115g/4oz 'no pre-cook' lasagne

25g/1oz cornflour

2.5ml/½ level teaspoon dry mustard

Pinch cayenne pepper

575ml/1 pint skimmed milk

40g/1½oz strong Cheddar cheese

Brown ground beef in a non-stick pan, drain off any fat. Remove and discard all visible fat from gammon and dice lean. Chop onion, slice celery and mushrooms. Remove and discard pith and seeds from pepper and chop flesh. Add vegetables and gammon to beef with tomatoes, stock cube, crushed garlic and herbs. Bring to boil. Cover and simmer for 45 minutes, removing the lid for the last 10 minutes. Place half the meat mixture in an ovenproof dish (about 20 x 25cm/8 x 10in) and cover with lasagne. Repeat. Blend together cornflour, dry mustard and cayenne pepper in a little cold skimmed milk. Mix with remaining milk, bring to boil and cook for 1 minute, stirring all the time. Grate the cheese and stir half into the sauce. Pour over the lasagne. Sprinkle the remaining grated cheese on top and cook at 200°C/400°F, gas mark 6, for 50 minutes.

HOW WERE the calories cut? We started with a meaty saving. Ordinary raw minced beef is about 65 calories per ounce. We used extra-lean ground beef, and browned it without traditional recipe's butter and/or oil. Calories then came down to around 45 per ounce.

WE MORE THAN halved the tomato cost, too. The 150g/5oz tomato purée in a traditional recipe would total 95 calories. We substituted a 400g/14oz can of tomatoes at only 40 calories.

INSTEAD OF THE usual streaky bacon, costing about 85 calories per raw ounce, we used lean gammon at only 25 calories an ounce. This is a big saving, yet you still get a fine flavour.

WE HALVED THE layers of lasagne: two is really quite enough. And we made the cheese sauce with skimmed milk and cornflour. No added double cream! But we bet you'll scarcely notice.

TRADITIONAL RECIPE
Serves 4 at 850 calories per portion

THIN TWIN
Serves 4 at 400 calories per portion

TUNA NOODLE CASSEROLE

Serves 4/380 calories per portion

115g/4oz tagliatelle

2 eggs, size 3

115g/4oz sweetcorn, frozen or canned

115g/4oz mushrooms

575ml/1 pint skimmed milk

15ml/1 level tablespoon chopped onion

60ml/4 level tablespoons cornflour

2.5ml/½ level teaspoon mustard

5ml/1 teaspoon lemon juice

2 x 198g cans tuna in brine

25g/1oz reduced-fat Cheddar cheese

25g/1oz fresh wholemeal breadcrumbs

Boil tagliatelle until just tender, then drain. Hard boil eggs. Cool in cold water; shell and slice. Boil frozen sweetcorn for 5 minutes. Slice mushrooms and place in a pan with most of the milk and onion. Cover and simmer gently for 5 minutes. Mix cornflour with remaining milk, then stir into the pan. Bring to the boil, stirring continuously, and simmer for 2 minutes. Season with salt, pepper, mustard and lemon juice. Drain and flake tuna. Stir into the sauce with the tagliatelle, eggs and sweetcorn. Turn into a heatproof dish. Grate cheese and mix with breadcrumbs. Cook at 200°C/400°F, gas mark 6, for 20 to 25 minutes.

The sauce would normally be made with full-fat milk, butter and flour. The mushrooms would be fried in extra butter, too. Tuna in oil would be used and the oil included in the dish. Full-fat cheese would be sprinkled on top. That adds up to around 800 calories a serving.

SPAGHETTI BOLOGNESE

Serves 4/410 calories per portion

225g/8oz very lean minced beef

15ml/1 level tablespoon flour

115g/4oz lean gammon steak

115g/4oz chicken livers

1 medium onion

115g/4oz mushrooms

115g/4oz carrots

1 clove garlic

1 beef stock cube

30ml/2 level tablespoons tomato purée

375ml/13floz boiling water

5ml/1 level teaspoon dried oregano

225g/8oz spaghetti

20ml/4 level teaspoons Parmesan cheese

Brown minced beef in a non-stick pan; drain off any fat. Transfer mince to a saucepan and stir in flour. Discarding all visible fat chop gammon. Trim and chop chicken livers. Add to mince. Chop onion and mushrooms. Finely dice carrot; crush garlic. Add to meat and mix well. Dissolve beef cube and tomato purée in the boiling water. Gradually add to the pan with oregano. Bring to the boil, stirring, then cover and simmer for 40 minutes. Boil spaghetti for 12 to 15 minutes. Drain and serve with bolognese sauce and sprinkled with Parmesan.

Lots of fat can get into a traditional bolognese sauce. The vegetables will be fried before adding to the meat and a fattier mince would be used and the fat not drained away.

SPAGHETTI ALLE VONGOLE

Serves 4/310 calories per portion

115g/4oz onion

1 clove garlic

425g/15oz can chopped tomatoes

150ml/¼ pint dry white wine

2.5ml/½ level teaspoon dried basil or 10ml/2 level teaspoons chopped fresh basil

10ml/2 level teaspoons cornflour

30ml/2 tablespoons water

2 x 290g cans baby clams in brine

Salt and pepper

225g/8oz spaghetti

Chop the onion and crush the garlic. Place in a saucepan with the tomatoes and their juice, wine and dried basil (if used). Bring to the boil and simmer uncovered for 20 minutes. Mix the cornflour with the water and then stir into the pan. Simmer for a minute, stirring continuously. Drain the clams and add to the pan with the fresh basil. Simmer for a few minutes longer. Season to taste. While the sauce is cooking boil the spaghetti until just tender. Drain and serve with the sauce.

An Italian chef would use lashings of oil to fry the onions and garlic and this dish could easily be 550 calories a serving.

TAGLIATELLE WITH MUSHROOMS

Serves 4/330 calories per portion

1 small onion

350g/12oz mushrooms

1 bay leaf

1 bouquet garni

575ml/1 pint semi-skimmed milk

25g/1oz cornflour

225g/8oz tagliatelle

60ml/4 level tablespoons fromage frais, 8% fat

Salt and pepper

Chop onion and slice mushrooms. Place in a pan with bay leaf, bouquet garni and most of the milk. Cover pan, leaving the lid slightly ajar, and simmer very gently for 5 minutes. Discard bay leaf and bouquet garni. Mix cornflour with the remaining milk and then stir into pan. Bring to boil, stirring, and simmer for a minute. Remove from heat. While mushrooms are cooking boil tagliatelle until just cooked. Drain. Stir fromage frais into the sauce and season well. Serve on pasta.

The mushroom and onion would normally be pre-fried in an ounce of butter – and that adds 210 calories to the recipe total. The sauce would also be made with full-fat milk, more butter, flour and cream. Made the Thin Twin way this tasty pasta dish costs about 265 fewer calories.

SPAGHETTI CARBONARA

275g/10oz wholewheat spaghetti

6 rashers streaky bacon

50g/2oz reduced-fat Cheddar cheese

2 eggs, size 3

45ml/3 level tablespoons Parmesan cheese

150ml/¼ pint reduced-fat single cream alternative

Cook spaghetti in boiling water. Well grill the bacon, then chop. Grate cheese. Beat eggs. Add half grated cheese and half Parmesan cheese. Drain the spaghetti and immediately return to the pan (off the heat) with bacon and Shape single cream. Add the egg and cheese mix. Stir well to coat the spaghetti – the heat of the spaghetti will cook the egg. Sprinkle the remaining grated cheese on top.

WHERE HAVE WE made the all-important calorie cuts? First, we've used fewer rashers of streaky bacon and grilled them first to remove much of the fat. Then we substituted reduced-fat hard cheese for ordinary hard cheese: that's about 80 calories chopped off for the 50g/2oz used in this Thin Twin recipe.

BY ADDING JUST TWO size-3 eggs instead of the usual two eggs plus two yolks, we've managed to slice off another 130 calories. Swapping a reduced-fat single cream alternative, such as St Ivel Shape single, for ordinary double or single cream makes great Thin Twin sense: you'll save 485 calories by leaving out double

cream and 150 calories by substituting for single.

TRADITIONAL RECIPES recommend you use 325g/12oz white spaghetti for four people; we reduced the amount to 275g/10oz and used wholewheat spaghetti (still makes four filling helpings) saving 190 calories.

ANY ITALIAN MAMA will add a great deal of butter to this dish; we haven't – and that saves a huge 210 calories for every ounce!

THEY'RE ALL SIMPLE, easy moves which carve hundreds of calories from this favourite dish – and we dare you to taste a difference!

TRADITIONAL RECIPE
Using double cream, 1,040 calories a portion; using single cream, 955 calories
THIN TWIN
Serves 4 at 455 calories per portion

THIN TWIN

CHEESE SOUFFLÉ

Serves 4/260 calories per portion

5ml/1 level teaspoon butter
**75g/3oz reduced-fat full-flavoured
Cheddar cheese**
40g/1½oz low-fat spread
40g/1½oz flour
275ml/½ pint skimmed milk
2.5ml/½ level teaspoon made mustard
4 eggs, size 2
Salt and pepper

Pre-heat the oven to 200°C/400°F, gas mark 6. Grease a 6 to 7-inch soufflé dish with the butter. Grate the cheese. Place the low-fat spread, flour and milk in a pan and whisk over a moderate heat until boiling. Simmer for a minute, whisking all the time. Add cheese and mustard. Separate eggs and whisk the yolks into the sauce one at a time. Season with salt and pepper. Whisk the egg whites until stiff but not dry – they should still be glossy. Gently fold one good tablespoon of whites into the sauce mixture. Add the remaining egg whites and fold in very gently. Turn mixture into the prepared dish and bake for about 30 minutes or until well risen and cooked in the centre. Serve immediately.

This light and fluffy meal made to a traditional recipe could easily add up to 380 calories. In this Thin Twin we've cut calories by making the soufflé with skimmed milk and low-fat spread. And the cheese is reduced-fat instead of the high-calorie standard Cheddar.

CHICKEN MARYLAND

Serves 4/450 calories per portion

4 x 115g/4oz chicken breast fillets
2 eggs, size 3
15g/½oz butter
115g/4oz wholemeal breadcrumbs
2 small bananas
50g/2oz plain flour
50ml/2floz skimmed milk
**115g/4oz sweetcorn, canned, frozen or
fresh kernels**
5ml/1 level teaspoon oil
2 rashers back bacon, rindless
225g/8oz French beans, frozen or fresh

Discard skin from chicken. Beat one egg. Gently melt butter, beat into egg. Dip chicken into egg then roll in breadcrumbs. Chill for 30 minutes. Bake at 190°C/375°F, gas mark 5, for 30 minutes. Bake bananas in their skins alongside the chicken for the last 10 minutes (trim a small piece off each end to prevent bursting). Put flour and a pinch of salt, remaining egg and milk into a processor and blend to form a smooth batter. Stir in sweetcorn. Heat oil in a non-stick pan and fry four fritters for 2 minutes on each side. Halve bacon rashers, form into a roll and grill well. Peel baked bananas, then halve. Serve chicken with bananas, fritters, bacon rolls and boiled beans.

This traditional American recipe is so high in fat that the calories are a horror story. We used skinless chicken breast fillets, and instead of deep-frying, we baked the crumbed pieces. We fried the sweetcorn fritters with just one teaspoon oil and baked the bananas. Making it the Thin Twin way cuts 550 calories a portion!

EGGS FLORENTINE

Serves 4/330 calories per portion

675g/1½lb frozen leaf spinach
Salt, pepper and small pinch nutmeg
8 eggs, size 3
30ml/2 level tablespoons cornflour
400ml/14floz skimmed milk
75g/3oz full-flavoured reduced-fat
Cheddar cheese
Pinch dry mustard
25g/1oz fresh wholemeal breadcrumbs

Cook the spinach, then drain thoroughly. Season with salt and pepper and nutmeg. Spread over the base of an ovenproof dish. Keep warm. Poach the eggs and arrange on top. While the eggs are poaching make the sauce. Mix the cornflour with a little milk until smooth. Heat the remaining milk until almost boiling, then pour onto the cornflour mixture, stirring continuously. Return to the pan and bring to the boil, stirring all the time. Grate cheese and add about three-quarters to the sauce. Season with salt, pepper and mustard. Pour sauce over eggs and sprinkle the remaining cheese and the breadcrumbs on top. Brown under the grill and serve immediately.

A little butter and cream is normally added to the cooked spinach. The sauce would be made with whole milk instead of skimmed; butter and flour instead of cornflour. A full-fat mature Cheddar would be used, too. So a traditional recipe could easily add up to 565 calories more than this Thin Twin version.

SPANISH OMELET

Serves 2/275 calories per portion

50g/2oz lean gammon
25g/1oz onion
50g/2oz frozen peas
115g/4oz cooked potato
50g/2oz canned pimento
4 eggs, size 3
20ml/4 teaspoons water
5ml/1 teaspoon olive oil

Grill the gammon, then discard any visible fat and cut the lean into small pieces. Finely chop the onion. Boil the peas as instructed on the packet. Dice the potato and pimento. Lightly beat eggs and water together. Heat oil in a non-stick omelet pan and cook the onion until soft. Add the gammon and vegetables and stir until evenly distributed. Pour into the eggs and cook until the bottom is firm but the top is still moist. Place under a hot grill until the top is just set. Serve flat.

In a traditional Spanish recipe, raw potato is first cooked in oil, then the eggs are added. The omelet would absorb about 480 oily calories. Our Thin Twin uses boiled potatoes and the minimum amount of oil for frying. We also used lean gammon instead of fatty bacon. The saving is 270 calories a portion.

MACARONI CHEESE

175g/6oz macaroni

75g/3oz reduced-fat Cheddar cheese

25g/1oz matured Cheddar cheese

175g/6oz mushrooms

4 medium tomatoes

45ml/3 level tablespoons cornflour

575ml/1 pint skimmed milk

75g/3oz wholemeal breadcrumbs

Salt and pepper

5ml/1 level teaspoon made mustard

Boil macaroni for 10 minutes in salted water. Drain and keep warm. Grate cheeses; slice mushrooms and tomatoes. To make sauce, blend the cornflour with a little cold milk. Heat remainder of the milk to boiling point and pour over the cornflour mixture, stirring continuously. Return milk to pan, bring to boil and simmer for 1-2 minutes. Season to taste and mix in the mustard and most of the cheese. Add the macaroni, mushrooms and tomatoes and transfer to an ovenproof serving dish. Sprinkle with the remaining cheese and breadcrumbs, then bake at 200°C/400°F, gas mark 6, for 20 minutes.

FOR FOUR PEOPLE, it is usual to cook 225g/8oz macaroni at a cost of 840 calories. We cut this amount down to 175g/6oz, and bulked up with mushrooms (24 calories) and tomatoes (48 calories). This way we gained flavour and lost 80 calories.

THE TRADITIONAL BASE to thicken the sauce is made with a roux of 75g/3oz butter at 630 calories and 90ml/6 level tablespoons flour at 180 calories – that totals 810 calories before the milk is added! Our Thin Twin sauce is thickened with cornflour costing just 100 calories. No butter needed! Result: a big saving of 710 calories.

USUAL RECIPES call for no less than 700ml/1¼ pints full cream milk, costing 475 calories. But because we have cut down on macaroni, and tomatoes and mushrooms produce some liquid

in the cooking, just 575ml/1 pint skimmed milk costing 190 calories is enough. This, mixed with cornflour, makes plenty of thick white sauce and saves 285 calories.

NO LESS THAN 225g/8oz matured Farmhouse Cheddar cheese at 146 calories an ounce – adding up to a horrifying 1170 calories – is normal in average recipes. Just half the quantity, made up of 75g/3oz reduced-fat Cheddar at 80 calories an ounce and 25g/1oz matured Cheddar gives a very good cheesy flavour and saves 385 calories.

THIS DISH DESERVES a good crunchy topping, so we splashed out 180 calories on wholemeal breadcrumbs. Mixed with grated cheese, then baked, this makes one of the crunchiest and flavoursome toppings of all.

TRADITIONAL RECIPE
Serves 4 at 800 calories per portion

THIN TWIN
Serves 4 at 355 calories per portion

VEGETABLE LASAGNE

Serves 4/300 calories per portion

1 medium onion, chopped

1 clove garlic, crushed

115g/4oz carrots, sliced

550g can passata (sieved tomatoes)

115g/4oz mushrooms, sliced

115g/4oz courgettes, sliced

1 small red pepper

5ml/1 level teaspoon dried basil

10ml/2 level teaspoons cornflour

25g/1oz low-fat spread

25g/1oz flour

400ml/14floz skimmed milk

75g/3oz reduced-fat Cheddar

75g/3oz no-need-to-pre-cook lasagne

Put onion, garlic and carrots in a saucepan with passata. Cover and simmer for 15 minutes. Add mushrooms, courgettes and deseeded chopped pepper with basil. Cover and cook for 5 minutes. Mix cornflour with a little cold water, then stir into pan. Bring to the boil and simmer for 2 minutes. Place low-fat spread and flour in a clean pan with the milk. Bring to the boil whisking all the time and simmer for a minute. Grate cheese and add most to the sauce. Season both sauces to taste. Arrange layers of vegetables, lasagne and cheese sauce in a shallow ovenproof dish finishing with sauce. Sprinkle remaining cheese on top. Bake at 190°C/375°F, gas mark 5, for 25 to 35 minutes.

The vegetables are not pre-fried and the sauce is made with skimmed milk and low-fat spread instead of whole milk and butter. The cheese is fat-reduced and because it is full-flavoured, a smaller amount is used. This cuts the traditional calories down from 500 to 300 a portion.

QUICHE LORRAINE

Serves 4/280 calories per portion

115g/4oz self-raising flour

32g/1 1/4oz low-fat spread

22g/3/4oz butter or margarine

25ml/5 teaspoons water

1/2 medium onion

50g/2oz mushrooms

50g/2oz lean gammon

50g/2oz reduced-fat Cheddar cheese

150ml/1/4 pint skimmed milk

2 eggs, size 3

1 egg white

Place flour in a bowl. Rub in low-fat spread and butter until the mixture resembles fine breadcrumbs. Add water and bind together. Roll pastry out thinly on a floured surface and use to line a 210cm/8 1/4in flan tin or ring. Prick the base a number of times and bake blind at 170°C/325°F, gas mark 3, for 10 minutes. Meanwhile chop onion and slice mushrooms. Remove and discard any visible fat from gammon, then dice the lean. Grate cheese. Lightly beat together skimmed milk and 2 eggs. Remove flan from oven and brush the inside with a little egg white. Scatter onion, mushrooms, gammon and cheese in the flan case. Pour egg mixture over and return to the oven at 180°C/350°F, gas mark 4, for 30-35 minutes. Serve hot or cold.

Here we've created a lower fat pastry base which immediately trimmed hundreds of calories from a traditional quiche. The filling is made with lower fat ingredients, too. A traditional quiche slice could easily add up to 680 calories. The Twin Twin saves 400 calories per portion.

CURRIED LENTIL RISSOLES

Serves 4/270 calories per portion

1 medium onion

225g/8oz split red lentils

1 bay leaf

575ml/1 pint water

5ml/1 level teaspoon butter

5ml/1 teaspoon oil

5ml/1 level teaspoon ground coriander

2.5ml/½ level teaspoon ground cumin

7.5ml/1½ level teaspoons curry powder

10ml/2 level teaspoons grated fresh root ginger

1 egg, size 3

75g/3oz fresh wholemeal breadcrumbs

Chop onion and place in a pan with rinsed and drained lentils, bay leaf and water. Cover pan, bring to boil and simmer gently for 40 minutes. Stir frequently while cooking and add a little extra water if necessary to prevent sticking. If there is any excess water left after cooking, uncover for a few minutes longer to allow it to evaporate. Heat butter and oil in a clean small pan. Stir in the coriander, cumin and curry powder. Cook, stirring, for 2 to 3 minutes. Mix with lentils, ginger and a pinch of salt. Leave to cool slightly. Lightly beat eggs and add half to lentil mixture. Shape into 8 flat cakes. Coat using remaining egg and breadcrumbs. Place on a baking sheet and cook in a preheated oven at 200°C/400°F, gas mark 6, for about 15 minutes.

We've used just a little butter and oil to make up these rissoles – a vegetarian cookbook may well suggest you use four times this amount. And you would normally be told to fry rather than cook the rissoles in the oven without fat and that saves hundreds more calories.

VEGETABLE CURRY

Serves 4/320 calories per portion

1 clove garlic

1 medium onion

10ml/2 teaspoons oil

15ml/1 level tablespoon curry powder

575ml/1 pint water

30ml/2 level tablespoons tomato purée

225g/8oz new potatoes

225g/8oz cauliflower

175g/6oz carrots

225g/8oz frozen peas

425g/15oz can chick peas

10ml/2 level teaspoons cornflour

150ml/¼ pint low-fat natural yogurt

Crush garlic and chop onion. Heat oil in a pan and add curry powder. Stir for 1 minute. Add water, tomato purée, garlic and onion. Bring to the boil, stirring occasionally. Scrub potatoes if new and halve any large ones. If old potatoes are used weigh when peeled and then cut into large chunks. Cut cauliflower into florets and slice carrots. Add potatoes, cauliflower and carrot to pan. Cover, bring to boil and simmer for 20 minutes. Add frozen peas and drained chick peas, cover and simmer for another 10 minutes. Stir occasionally while cooking and add a little extra water if necessary. Mix cornflour with a little extra water and stir into the curry. Simmer, stirring, for a few minutes. Add yogurt and reheat but do not boil.

We used just 10ml/2 teaspoons oil to fry the curry powder. The vegetables can be cooked in the sauce. We've not added coconut milk to the sauce – the flavour is good without it – and we have used a low-fat yogurt instead of the creamier sort.

BOEUF BOURGUIGNON

575g/1¼lb lean, good quality braising steak

115g/4oz lean gammon

225g/8oz button onions

1 bay leaf

1 bouquet garni

1 clove garlic

275ml/½ pint dry red wine

1 beef stock cube

150ml/¼ pint hot water

15ml/1 level tablespoon tomato purée

45ml/3 level tablespoons cornflour

225g/8oz button mushrooms

Remove and discard any visible fat from the beef and the gammon. Cube the lean. Place in a large casserole dish with the peeled onions, bay leaf, bouquet garni, crushed garlic, wine, stock cube, water and tomato purée. Cover and cook at 180˚C/350˚F, gas mark 4, for 1¾ hours. Blend cornflour with a little cold water and stir into casserole with mushrooms. Cook for a further 30 minutes.

FIRST, WE PICKED lean good quality braising steak and trimmed off all visible fat. The classic recipe would use a fattier untrimmed beef and the lean swap saves 16 calories per ounce and a whole 320 calories in the total recipe.

IF YOU USE streaky bacon in any casserole recipe all the fat that you would normally grill away goes straight into the dish. We used lean gammon instead of the traditional bacon and lost none of this French classic's flavour but saved 175 calories.

FLOUTING TRADITION we didn't pre-fry the meat in fat. All the fatty juices are usually tipped into the casserole and end up adding lots of calories to the total.

WE USED slightly less beef and added more onions and mushrooms. This not only saves calories, but increases the vegetable content of the recipe in a healthy way.

SIMPLE SUBSTITUTIONS like these means you can halve the calories in this haute cuisine dish yet it still tastes trés terrific.

TRADITIONAL RECIPE
Serves 4 at 655 calories per portion

THIN TWIN
Serves 4 at 305 calories per portion

BEEF STROGANOFF

Serves 4/240 calories per portion

450g/1lb lean grilling steak (fillet or rump or sirloin)

115g/4oz onion

225g/8oz button mushrooms

7g/¼oz butter

10ml/2 teaspoons oil

275g/10oz natural low-fat yogurt

10ml/2 level teaspoons cornflour

10ml/2 level teaspoons French mustard

10ml/2 level teaspoons tomato purée

Salt and pepper

Discard all visible fat from the beef and cut lean into strips no bigger than your little finger. Thinly slice the onion and separate into rings. Slice the mushrooms. Heat butter and oil in a large non-stick frying pan with a lid. Add the onions, cover and cook over a low heat for 10 minutes or until soft. Add the mushrooms, cover again, and cook over a low heat for about 3 minutes. Uncover the pan and raise the heat. Cook, stirring frequently, until onions and mushrooms are golden. Remove the vegetables from the pan with a slotted spoon. Keep warm. Add the beef to the pan and cook over a fairly high heat until just cooked – about 6 to 8 minutes. Mix a little yogurt with the cornflour until smooth. Add remaining yogurt, mustard and tomato purée. Season. Add the vegetables to the beef in the pan and stir in the yogurt mixture. Heat, stirring continuously, until the sauce just boils. Serve.

In this Thin Twin the minimum amount of fat is used to fry the onion and mushrooms. Keeping the lid on and using a non-stick pan means they can soften and cook with just a little fat. Low-fat yogurt is used instead of soured cream, and the cornflour prevents it curdling.

BEEF GOULASH

Serves 4/210 calories per portion

450g/1lb lean braising beef

15ml/1 level tablespoon paprika

225g/8oz onions

115g/4oz carrots

1 small red pepper

400g can chopped tomatoes

1 beef stock cube

75g/3oz Greek yogurt

Discard all visible fat from the beef and cut the lean into bite-size pieces. Place in a casserole dish and sprinkle on the paprika. Chop the onion and slice the carrots. Deseed and chop the pepper. Add the onion, carrots, pepper and tomatoes to the meat. Crumble the stock cube and stir in. Cover and cook at 150°C/300°F, gas mark 2, for 3 hours. Swirl the yogurt on top and serve.

In a traditional recipe fattier beef would be used. The vegetables and meat would be cooked in fat (about 450 calories worth). Sour cream would be used instead of yogurt. Saving – 330 calories a portion.

RENDANG

Serves 4/230 calories per portion

40g/1½oz creamed coconut

150ml/¼ pint boiling water

115g/4oz onion

2 cloves garlic

30ml/2 level tablespoons chopped fresh root ginger

5ml/1 level teaspoon chilli powder

5ml/1 level teaspoon ground coriander

2.5ml/½ level teaspoon turmeric

2.5ml/½ level teaspoon salt

5ml/1 level teaspoon dried lemon grass

115ml/4floz cold water

450g/1lb lean braising steak

Grate the creamed coconut into a bowl and pour on the boiling water. Stir to dissolve. Roughly chop onion; crush garlic. Place onion and garlic in a liquidizer or food processor with the ginger, chilli powder, coriander, turmeric, salt and lemon grass. Add the coconut milk and blend to make a paste. Turn the paste into a fairly large saucepan. Rinse the machine out with the cold water and add to the pan. Cut beef into bite-sized pieces, discarding all visible fat. Add to the pan and mix well. Simmer gently, uncovered for 2½ hours, stirring frequently. This is a 'dry' curry and when cooked the sauce should have reduced to a thick paste. If the mixture dries up before it is cooked, add a little extra water to prevent it sticking.

In the original recipe for this Indonesian Beef Curry the onions and meat would be fried in ghee (clarified butter which is 235 calories an ounce) or oil. The creamed coconut is reduced from 115g/4oz to 40g/1½oz, saving 235 calories.

NAVARIN OF LAMB

Serves 4/240 calories per portion

450g/1lb lean, boneless leg of lamb

175g/6oz shallots or 1 medium onion

175g/6oz small turnips

175g/6oz carrots

1 clove garlic

1 lamb or beef stock cube

30ml/2 level tablespoons tomato purée

15ml/1 level tablespoon mushroom ketchup

Few drops gravy browning

1 bouquet garni

225g/8oz small new potatoes

15ml/1 level tablespoon cornflour

50g/2oz frozen peas

Discarding visible fat, cube lamb. Plunge shallots into boiling water for 1 minute. Drain and peel. Or chop onion. Quarter turnips; slice carrots. Crush garlic. Place lamb and vegetables in a large casserole dish. Dissolve stock cube, tomato purée, mushroom ketchup and gravy browning in boiling water. Pour over meat and vegetables. Add bouquet garni. Cover and cook at 170°C/325°F, gas mark 3, for 1 hour. Scrub potatoes and halve or quarter. Add to casserole and cook for 30 minutes. Mix cornflour with a little water; stir into casserole. Add the frozen peas. Cover and cook for another 30 minutes. Discard bouquet garni before serving.

Fatty middle neck of lamb is often used in this classic French recipe. By using lean leg of lamb you can save 220 calories a portion. Calories are also saved by not pre-frying vegetables and using cornflour instead of a roux to thicken. Total savings amount to 300 calories a portion.

THIN TWIN

LAMB HOT POT

4 boneless lamb chump steaks, extra-trimmed, 115g/4oz each

2 lamb's kidneys

5ml/1 level teaspoon dried thyme

150g/5oz carrots

115g/4oz mushrooms

225g/8oz onions

1 lamb or beef stock cube

15ml/1 level tablespoon tomato chutney

15ml/1 level tablespoon mushroom ketchup

450g/1lb peeled potatoes

Grill steaks on both sides until cooked, then place in a casserole dish (save fat that cooks out). Cut each kidney into eight, discarding cores. Add to steaks; sprinkle with thyme. Thinly slice carrots, mushrooms and onions, then arrange on meat. Dissolve stock cube in 425ml/¾ pint boiling water, add tomato chutney and mushroom ketchup, then pour over vegetables. Season with salt and pepper. Slice potatoes and arrange overlapping to cover top. Take 5ml/1 level teaspoon of fat reserved from steaks, and brush over potato. Cover with non-stick baking paper and cook at 325°C/170°F, gas mark 3, for 1½ hours. Remove paper for last 30 minutes to crisp the potatoes.

WHY IS ORDINARY Hot Pot so horribly high in calories? The traditional recipe calls for double the weight of fatty middle-neck chops: that's at least 2,305 calories before anything else is added! We substituted nicely lean extra-trimmed chump steaks for these which, because they are boneless, give very nearly the same amount of meat. As they are trimmed of fat, they are far lower in calories.

WE GRILLED OUR STEAKS thoroughly before adding to the casserole. Prepared this way, our lean meat steaks come to just 780 calories.

TRADITIONAL RECIPES have only potatoes and onions added to the meat. Our version adds carrots and mushrooms for extra flavour. At 5 calories an ounce for carrots and 4 calories for mushrooms, our dish gets bulk for around 40 calories –

instead of 205 calories for the same amount of potatoes.

THE FATTY GRAVY of the classic recipes that comes from cooking fatty meat with vegetables in water is not to be recommended. Our delicious low-calorie version combines the flavours of mushroom ketchup and tomato chutney mingled with a stock cube base for a mere 70 calories.

NO HOT POT is complete without its sliced potato topping. We halved the amount of potatoes used to top the dish and saved 365 calories. And the 28g/1oz dripping (253 calories!) recommended in traditional recipes for brushing on the potatoes can be easily reduced. Just 5ml/1 level teaspoon of the fat from the grilled steaks is all you need to get a crispy and tasty potato top – for a cost of just 40 calories.

TRADITIONAL RECIPE
Serves 4 at 770 calories per portion

THIN TWIN
Serves 4 at 355 calories per portion

PORK SATAY

Serves 4/230 calories per portion

450g/1lb pork fillet

2 small onions

1 clove garlic

45ml/3 tablespoons lemon juice

45ml/3 tablespoons water plus 150ml/¼ pint water

5ml/1 level teaspoon grated fresh root ginger

60ml/4 tablespoons dark soy sauce

10ml/2 level teaspoons soft brown sugar

40g/1½oz crunchy peanut butter

2.5ml/½ level teaspoon chilli powder

Discard any fat or sinew from pork, then cut into cubes. Slice one onion and crush garlic. Place in a dish with lemon juice, 45ml/3 tablespoons water, ginger, 45ml/3 tablespoons dark soy sauce and 5ml/1 level teaspoon sugar. Stir well to dissolve sugar, then add pork. Turn all the pieces over in the marinade. Cover and leave in the refrigerator for at least 1 hour or up to 12 hours. Drain meat from the marinade and scrape off as much grated ginger as possible. Thread pork onto four skewers and cook under a preheated grill for about 10 minutes or until cooked through. Turn once or twice while cooking. Finely chop remaining onion and place in a small pan with 150ml/¼ pint water, peanut butter, chilli powder, 15ml/1 tablespoon soy sauce and 5ml/1 level teaspoon sugar. Cover and simmer for 10 minutes. Serve sauce with pork.

Pork fillet is very lean and is as low calorie as chicken. A fattier cut of pork would traditionally be used and the marinade include oil. The sauce would normally be made with more peanut butter, oil and sugar. So this traditional Indonesian dish could easily cost 600 calories a portion.

SWEET AND SOUR PORK

Serves 4/240 calories per portion

350g/12oz pork fillet or tenderloin

15ml/1 tablespoon dry sherry

45ml/3 tablespoons light soy sauce

10ml/2 level teaspoons cornflour

1 red and 1 green pepper

175g/6oz carrots

6 spring onions

227g/8oz can pineapple in juice

15ml/1 tablespoon vinegar

15ml/1 level tablespoon sugar

15ml/1 level tablespoon tomato purée

⅓ chicken stock cube

15ml/1 tablespoon oil

225g/8oz beansprouts

Discarding fat from pork, cut lean into strips. Mix sherry with 15ml/1 tablespoon soy sauce and 5ml/1 level teaspoon cornflour. Add pork and mix well. Leave for 20 minutes. Cut deseeded red and green pepper, carrots and trimmed spring onions into strips. Drain pineapple (reserve juice) and cut into pieces. Mix vinegar, sugar, tomato purée and stock cube with 75ml/3floz hot water. Add remaining soy sauce. Mix cornflour with juice and add. Make up to 175ml/6floz with water. Heat oil in a non-stick pan. Add pork and stir fry for 5 minutes. Add peppers, carrots and spring onions. Stir fry for 3 minutes. Add pineapple, beansprouts and sauce. Bring to boil and cook for 1 minute.

Instead of being coated in batter and deep-fried, the meat is marinaded for extra flavour. The minimum of oil is used to stir fry. That means this Thin Twin is 620 calories a portion lower than a traditional recipe.

PORK CHOPS NORMANDY

Serves 4/245 calories per portion

4 x 115g/4oz boneless loin pork chops, well trimmed

275ml/½ pint dry cider

275ml/½ pint water

½ chicken stock cube

2 eating apples

10ml/2 level teaspoons cornflour

15ml/1 level tablespoon chopped parsley

45ml/3 level tablespoons fromage frais, 0% fat

Grill chops until cooked through. Place in a pan with the cider and water and stock cube. Cover, bring to the boil and simmer gently for 20 minutes. Remove chops and keep warm. Peel, core and slice the apples very thickly. Add to the pan and simmer very gently until tender but still holding their shape. Remove with a slotted spoon and arrange around the pork. Keep warm. Boil liquid rapidly, uncovered, until reduced to 275ml/½ pint. Mix the cornflour with a little cold water until smooth. Add to pan, whisking continuously, and simmer for a few minutes. Remove from heat and whisk in chopped parsley and the fromage frais. Pour over chops and serve.

The chops would normally be fried and the fatty juices added to the sauce. Instead we grill the chops and if any fat is marbled through it will melt into the grill pan. We also thicken the sauce with cornflour instead of butter and flour and use fromage frais instead of cream. Savings would be about 300 per portion.

BARBECUED PORK

Serves 4/225 calories per portion

450g/1lb pork fillet

7g/¼oz butter

30ml/2 tablespoons light soy sauce

15ml/1 tablespoon Worcestershire sauce

60ml/4 level tablespoons tomato ketchup

15ml/1 level tablespoon brown fruity sauce

15ml/1 level tablespoon honey

5ml/1 level teaspoon French mustard

5ml/1 teaspoon oil

1 medium onion

⅓ chicken stock cube

2 medium tomatoes

Discard any fat from pork, then cut lean into thick slices. Melt butter and mix with soy sauce, Worcestershire sauce, tomato ketchup, brown fruity sauce, honey and mustard. Add pork and turn the pieces around so that they are well coated. Cover and refrigerate for 2 to 3 hours. Remove pork from marinade. Heat oil in a non-stick frying pan, add pork and cook until it changes colour on all sides. Transfer to a saucepan. Chop onion and add to pan with 150ml/¼ pint water and stock cube. Cover and simmer for 30 minutes; stir occasionally. Remove pork and keep warm. Add marinade to pan and boil, uncovered, until it is thick. Skin the tomatoes, halve and squeeze out seeds. Roughly chop tomatoes and add to sauce. Simmer for 2 to 3 minutes. Mix with the pork and serve.

The cut of pork would normally be a fattier one, and it would be cooked in far more oil and all the fatty juices would go into the sauce. If you wish you could cube the marinaded pork and grill it, then serve with barbecue sauce.

MOUSSAKA

450g/1lb aubergines

225g/8oz potatoes, peeled weight

450g/1lb extra-lean minced beef

1 large onion

1 clove garlic

400g/14oz can chopped tomatoes

15ml/1 level tablespoon tomato purée

1.25ml/¼ teaspoon nutmeg

30ml/2 tablespoons chopped parsley

Salt and pepper

2 egg yolks, size 3

275g/10oz low-fat natural yogurt

25g/1oz reduced-fat Cheddar cheese

Finely slice aubergines and place immediately in boiling salted water for 2-3 minutes. Remove, drain and set aside. Finely slice potatoes and blanch in boiling salted water for 5 minutes. Drain and set aside. Cook extra-lean minced beef in a non-stick pan until evenly browned (about 3-4 minutes). Drain off any fat that cooks out. Return to medium heat and add finely chopped onion and crushed garlic. Cook for 2 minutes, then add tomatoes, tomato purée, nutmeg, chopped parsley and the seasoning. Mix well and heat hrough. Place half the blanched aubergines in the bottom of a 1.7 litre/3 pint ovenproof dish.

Pour over half the meat mixture, then top with half the potatoes. Repeat layers once more. Beat egg yolks and yogurt together. Pour this sauce evenly over the potato topping. Sprinkle with the grated cheese. Bake the Moussaka at 190°C/375°F, gas mark 5, for approximately 45 minutes or until the top is golden brown.

INSTEAD OF FRYING the aubergines in oil, we softened them by blanching in boiling water – and saved 480 calories.

WE USED EXTRA-LEAN minced beef instead of fatty lamb in our Thin Twin Moussaka which gives a saving of at least 80 calories.

THE ORIGINAL RECIPE fries the meat in 30ml/2 tablespoons oil. Cooking it in a non-stick pan needs no oil at all, and gives another good saving of 240 calories.

TRADITIONAL COOKS use 675g/1½lb meat. Our Thin Twin recipe cuts this to 450g/1lb and makes up the difference with 225g/½lb potatoes. Potatoes absorb the flavours beautifully – and give a saving of 225 calories per serving.

THE MOUSSAKA SAUCE is usually made with rich Greek yogurt (33 calories per 25g/1oz). Low-fat natural yogurt (costs 15 calories per 25g/1oz), tastes just as good and saves 180 calories.

TWO SIZE-2 EGGS (180 calories) are used in the original recipe; but it's the yolks that give the sauce its rich texture. By using just the yolks of two smaller size-3 eggs, we saved 50 calories.

REDUCED-FAT CHEDDAR cheese is sprinkled on top instead of 25g/1oz Parmesan, saving 50 calories.

TRADITIONAL RECIPE
Serves 4 at 745 calories per portion

THIN TWIN RECIPE
Serves 4 at 360 calories per portion

PORK FILLET WITH PRUNES

Serves 4/290 calories per portion

115g/4oz ready-to-eat dried prunes

275ml/½ pint dry white wine

450g/1lb pork fillet

5ml/1 level teaspoon butter

1 shallot or small onion

½ chicken stock cube

30ml/2 tablespoons port

15ml/1 level tablespoon redcurrant jelly

90ml/6 level tablespoons powdered skimmed milk

Soak the prunes in the wine for about 30 minutes. Discard any fat from the pork fillet and cut into 1-inch slices. Melt the butter in a non-stick pan and brown the pork on all sides. Chop the shallot or onion and add to the pan with the stock cube, prunes and wine. Cover the pan, bring to the boil and simmer for about 25 minutes. Remove the pork and prunes and keep warm. Measure the liquid. You should have 150ml/¼ pint. If there is too much boil it rapidly, uncovered, to reduce. Stir the port and redcurrant jelly into the cooking liquid. Mix the skimmed milk powder with a little warm (not hot) water until smooth. Stir into the sauce and reheat. Pour over the meat and serve.

Pork fillet is lower in calories than the loin of pork usually used in this dish. This would be made with much more butter and up to 225ml/8floz double cream (a horrific 1,000 calories). Skimmed milk powder gives a creamy flavour for just 110 calories.

CARBONNADE OF BEEF

Serves 4/330 calories per portion

40g/1½oz smoked, lean streaky bacon

450g/1lb lean braising beef

225g/8oz onion

1 clove garlic

1 beef stock cube

115ml/4floz boiling water

5ml/1 level teaspoon brown sugar

275ml/½ pint beer

15ml/1 tablespoon vinegar

1 bouquet garni

15ml/1 level tablespoon cornflour

115g/4oz French bread

10ml/2 level teaspoons French mustard

Grill bacon, then cut into small pieces. Discard all visible fat from the beef and cut lean into bite-size pieces. Chop onion and crush the garlic. Place bacon, beef, onion and garlic in a casserole dish. Dissolve the stock cube and sugar in the boiling water. Add to the casserole with the vinegar, beer and bouquet garni. Cover and cook at 150°C/300°F, gas mark 2, for 3 hours. Mix the cornflour with a little cold water, then stir into the casserole. Cover and cook for another 15 minutes. Cut bread into 4 slices and spread with the mustard. Place mustard side up on top of casserole and press down so that it absorbs the gravy. Cook, uncovered, for a further 30 minutes.

You'll save about 140 calories when you cook a Carbonnade the Thin Twin way. The beef is lean in our recipe – a fattier one is used in a traditional recipe. No fat is used to pre-cook the meat and vegetables. The bacon is grilled first and fat discarded rather than fried and any fat included in the recipe.

CASSOULET

Serves 4/300 calories per portion

175g/6oz pork leg steak

175g/6oz lamb leg steak

115g/4oz gammon steak

1 clove garlic

1 medium onion

175g/6oz carrots

400g/14oz can chopped tomatoes

1 beef stock cube

150ml/¼ pint boiling water

1 bay leaf

425g/15oz can cannellini beans or white kidney beans

50g/2oz garlic sausage

15ml/1 level tablespoon cornflour

Discard all visible fat from the pork, lamb and gammon, then cube. Mix together in a casserole dish. Crush garlic, chop onion and slice carrots. Add to the meat with the tomatoes. Dissolve the stock cube in boiling water and add with the bay leaf. Cover the dish and cook at 170°C/325°F, gas mark 3, for 2½ hours. Drain the beans and cut the sausage into small cubes. Stir into the casserole and return to the oven for another 15 minutes. Mix the cornflour with a little cold water, then stir into the casserole. Cook for another 15 minutes. Discard the bay leaf before serving.

A Cassoulet would normally arrive at the table glistening with a fatty gravy. That's because pork belly, streaky bacon and fatty sausages would have been used instead of the lean meats we've chosen. More fat would have been added when the vegetables were pre-fried. A traditional portion could add up to 600 calories.

CORNED BEEF HASH

Serves 4/325 calories per portion

675g/1½lb potatoes, peeled weight

75g/3oz onion

75g/3oz streaky bacon

225g/8oz corned beef

115g/4oz cooked beetroot (not in vinegar)

30ml/2 tablespoons chopped parsley

45ml/3 level tablespoons fromage frais, 8% fat

Salt and pepper

5ml/1 level teaspoon bacon fat, saved from grilling the bacon

Cut the potato and onion into small chunks and boil together until tender. Drain and mash roughly. Grill the bacon until crisp, then cut into small pieces. Chop the corned beef and beetroot. Add to the potato mixture with the parsley and fromage frais. Season with salt and pepper. Brush the inside of an ovenproof dish with the bacon fat. Fill with the corned beef hash and level the top. Bake at 200°C/400°F, gas mark 6, for 25 to 30 minutes.

A Hash is usually a fry-up of leftover vegetables and meat. But a Hash can be a tasty meal to cook from raw, and reasonable in calories as long as you make it the Thin Twin way. Calories are cut by using the minimum of fat and cooking the Hash in the oven.

SHEPHERD'S PIE

450g/1lb potatoes, peeled weight

225g/8oz swede, peeled weight

450g/1lb extra lean minced beef

1 medium onion

30ml/2 level tablespoons flour

15ml/1 level tablespoon tomato purée

2.5ml/½ level teaspoon mixed herbs

1 beef stock cube

175ml/6floz hot water

50ml/2floz skimmed milk

Boil potatoes and swede until tender. Brown the ground beef in a non-stick frying pan; drain off the fat. Chop the onion and stir into the meat with flour, tomato purée and mixed herbs. Dissolve stock cube in hot water. Place meat in an ovenproof dish, pour over the stock. Mash the drained potatoes and swede with the skimmed milk. Spread or pipe the mixture over the meat. Cook at 190˚C/375˚F, gas mark 5, for 1 hour.

THIS FAMILY FAVOURITE can easily add up to almost twice the calories of our Thin Twin – and not be the least bit more satisfying or tasty a dish.

POTATOES WOULD normally be used for the mash topping. We substituted swede for a third of the potatoes. This saves 140 calories and added to the topping's flavour.

TRADITIONALLY LOTS OF butter and whole milk would also be used to make the mash. We omitted the butter and mashed the vegetables with a little skimmed milk instead. The total saving was 440 calories.

ABOUT DOUBLE the quantity of flour would have been used to thicken the stock in a traditional recipe. Our Thin Twin saves calories, too, by using stock cubes rather than a fatty beef stock.

WE USED extra lean minced beef and made sure that any fat that cooked out was thrown way. Traditionally a fatty mince would be used and extra fat added to fry the meat and vegetables. This would add 200 calories to the dish.

THE RESULT: a recipe that you could serve up to all the family without them realizing its a low calorie recipe. And our Thin Twin is very healthily low in fat, too.

TRADITIONAL RECIPE
Serves 4 at 600 calories per portion

THIN TWIN
Serves 4 at 320 calories per portion

SPANISH CHICKEN

Serves 4/230 calories per portion

4 chicken breasts, 175g/6oz each
1 medium onion
1 clove garlic
425ml/¾ pint passata (sieved tomatoes)
60ml/4 tablespoons dry sherry
1 red pepper
115g/4oz button mushrooms
40g/1½oz green olives
115g/4oz frozen petit pois

Skin the chicken breasts and place in a single layer in an ovenproof dish. Chop the onion and crush the garlic. Place in a saucepan with the passata and sherry. Simmer uncovered for 5 minutes. Deseed and slice the pepper, add to the pan and cook for 1 minute. Pour over the chicken. Cover and cook at 180°C/350°F, gas mark 4, for 30 minutes. Add the mushrooms, olives and petit pois and stir carefully to distribute evenly around the chicken. Cover and cook for another 20 minutes.

Any Spanish main course dish is likely to be cooked in lots of oil. We cut out oil completely by cooking the vegetables in the sauce. The chicken breasts would have had the skin left on, too.

TURKEY VERONIQUE

Serves 4/270 calories per portion

575g/1¼lb turkey breast fillets or escalopes
150ml/¼ pint dry white wine
150ml/¼ pint water
½ chicken stock cube
1 bay leaf
6 black peppercorns
1 small onion
115g/4oz grapes
30ml/2 level tablespoons cornflour
40g/1½oz skimmed milk powder
50g/2oz fromage frais, 8% fat
Few sprigs tarragon

Place turkey in an ovenproof dish with wine, water, stock cube, bay leaf, peppercorns and sliced onion. Cover and cook at 180°C/350°F, gas mark 4, for 1 hour. Discard bay leaf, peppercorns and onion. Pour cooking liquid into a measuring jug and make up to 375ml/13floz with water. Keep the meat warm. Halve grapes, discarding seeds. Place in a covered dish in the oven turned to low to warm through. Mix cornflour and powdered milk with a little warm water until completely smooth. Add to cooking liquid, stirring all the time, then pour into a pan and bring to the boil, stirring continuously. Simmer for 2 minutes. Remove from heat and whisk in the fromage frais. Stir in half the grapes. Arrange meat on a serving dish and pour the sauce over. Garnish with remaining grapes and tarragon.

Traditionally chicken quarters with skin would have been used. Using skinless turkey breasts saves about 350 calories. We have also kept calories low by making the sauce with skimmed milk powder and fromage frais rather than double cream.

ITALIAN STYLE MEATBALLS

Serves 4/350 calories per portion

400g/14oz can passata (sieved tomatoes)

227g/8oz can chopped tomatoes

75g/3oz onion

2 cloves garlic

10ml/2 level teaspoons dried oregano

2.5ml/½ level teaspoon dried basil

1 egg, size 3

450g/1lb extra lean minced beef

50g/2oz fresh wholemeal breadcrumbs

25g/1oz freshly grated Parmesan cheese

30ml/2 level tablespoons tomato ketchup

Salt and pepper

Place passata and chopped tomatoes in a sauce-pan. Finely chop onion and crush the garlic. Add all the onion and half the garlic to the pan with 5ml/1 level teaspoon oregano and the basil. Cover and simmer for 15 minutes. Lightly beat the egg and mix with the minced beef, breadcrumbs, Parmesan cheese, tomato ketchup and remaining garlic and oregano. Season well. Shape into 16 balls. Place in the sauce, adding one at a time and simmer, covered, for 30 minutes.

A fatty mince costs 65 calories an ounce instead of 55 calories for very lean mince. Traditionally meatballs would be fried in oil, too, and the sauce made with oil. In our recipe a little Parmesan is used to flavour the meatballs instead of a lot of cheese being sprinkled on top.

BEEF IN OYSTER SAUCE

Serves 4/220 calories per portion

450g/1lb lean grilling steak (rump or fillet or sirloin)

15ml/1 tablespoon light soy sauce

15ml/1 tablespoon dry sherry

10ml/2 level teaspoons cornflour

⅓ beef stock cube

150ml/¼ pint hot water

45ml/3 tablespoons oyster sauce

30ml/2 tablespoons cold water

4 spring onions

10ml/2 teaspoons oil

450g/1lb beansprouts

Cut the beef into small strips, discarding all visible fat. Mix together the soy sauce, sherry and 5ml/1 level teaspoon cornflour. Add the beef and mix well. Leave to marinade for 20 minutes. Dissolve the stock cube in the hot water with the oyster sauce. Mix the remaining 5ml/1 level teaspoon cornflour with the cold water, then add to the sauce mixture. Trim spring onions and slice diagonally. Heat oil in a non-stick wok or deep frying pan. Add the beef and stir until well browned on all sides. Add the beansprouts and the spring onions. Stir in the sauce mixture and bring to the boil, stirring all the time. Simmer for a minute and then serve.

A non-stick pan is essential so the minimum amount of oil can be used for stir frying. Beansprouts add bulk for a tiny calorie cost. A traditional Beef in Oyster Sauce would cost about 125 calories more a portion.

CHICKEN CORDON BLEU

4 boneless chicken breasts, 115g/4oz each

115g/4oz fresh wholemeal breadcrumbs

4 slices lean ham, 25g/1oz each

50g/2oz Boursin Cheese with Garlic and Herbs

20ml/4 level teaspoons plain flour

1 egg, size 3

5ml/1 teaspoon oil

Place each chicken breast between 2 sheets of non-stick paper and flatten with a rolling pin until doubled in size. Spread breadcrumbs over an ungreased baking tray and grill until crisp. Lay a piece of ham on top of each chicken breast and place a quarter of the cheese in the centre of this. Fold the chicken in to cover the cheese and to prevent 'oozing' during cooking. Form into a roll; secure with cocktail sticks and chill for 10 minutes. Beat the egg. Roll chicken in the flour, then in the egg and then in breadcrumbs so that it is evenly coated. Grease a baking tray with the oil and place chicken portions on it. Bake at 190°C/375°F, gas mark 5, for 45 minutes. Turn the portions over once during cooking and serve immediately.

CHICKEN IS such a lovely low calorie meat, that it is a crying shame for a chef to find so many ways to make its calories soar. When you cook a classic Chicken Cordon Bleu the filling is high calorie, the coating high calorie, and even more calories are added when the portions are deep fried.

THE FILLING would usually be made by blending 50g/2oz butter with the cheese. That would add 420 calories to the recipe's total.

THE SOFT CHEESE used in classic recipes would be higher fat and higher in calories, too. Boursin Cheese with Garlic and Herbs is very flavoursome and costs 116 calories per 25g/1oz compared to 130 calories for a richer cream cheese.

WHOLEMEAL breadcrumbs give the chicken an attractive coating and saves a few calories. Traditionally white breadcrumbs are used which are 5 calories an ounce more.

BEFORE THE CHICKEN portions are rolled in breadcrumbs they would normally be coated with melted butter. The 75g/3oz often recommended would add 630 calories. We coated the chicken with a small amount of flour and beaten egg at a cost of 120 calories. That saves 510 calories in total.

TO PILE ON even more calories a classic Chicken Cordon Bleu is deep fried. We baked without added fat and ended up with a crispy crumb jacket, tender chicken and a juicy, cheesy centre.

TRADITIONAL RECIPE
Serves 4 at 700 calories per portion

THIN TWIN
Serves 4 at 360 calories per portion

COQ AU VIN

Serves 4/305 calories per portion

4 chicken leg joints, 275g/10oz each
50g/2oz lean gammon
175g/6oz shallots or 1 medium onion
1 clove garlic
15ml/1 level tablespoon tomato purée
1 chicken stock cube
115ml/4floz boiling water
1 bouquet garni
1 bay leaf
275ml/½ pint red wine
225g/8oz button mushrooms
15ml/1 level tablespoon cornflour

Discard skin from chicken legs, then place them in a casserole dish. Grill the gammon. Discard all visible fat and cut the lean into small pieces. Add to the chicken. Blanch shallots in boiling water for 1 minute, then drain and peel. Or chop the onion. Crush garlic. Dissolve tomato purée and stock cube in boiling water. Add to the casserole with shallots or onion, garlic, bouquet garni, bay leaf and red wine. Cover and cook at 180°C/350°F, gas mark 4, for 1¼ hours. Add mushrooms, cover and cook for another ½ hour. Discard bouquet garni and bay leaf. Mix cornflour with cold water. Stir into the casserole and cook for 15 minutes.

When you throw away the skin from the chicken legs you discard 285 calories. In a traditional Coq au Vin the vegetables would have been fried and the sauce would have been thickened with a roux of flour and butter. Fatty bacon would also have been used instead of the leaner gammon. So you could easily have ended up in paying 680 calories for a portion.

CHICKEN MARENGO

Serves 4/215 calories per portion

4 chicken breasts, 175g/6oz each
5ml/1 teaspoon oil
75g/3oz onion
75g/3oz carrots
30ml/2 level tablespoons tomato purée
115ml/4floz dry sherry
275ml/½ pint water
1 chicken stock cube
115g/4oz button mushrooms
Chopped parsley

Discard skin from chicken breasts. Heat oil in a non-stick frying pan, then cook the chicken until golden brown on all sides. Finely chop onion and slice carrots. Add to the pan with tomato purée, sherry, water and crumbled stock cube. Cover and bring to the boil, then simmer gently for 25 minutes. Remove chicken. Purée the sauce in a blender or food processor or rub through a sieve. Return to the pan with the chicken and mushrooms and simmer for another 5 to 10 minutes. Sprinkle with parsley before serving.

Although you can discard skin from grilled or baked chicken after cooking, if you don't discard it before casseroling then lots of fatty calories will melt into the sauce. Calories have been reduced by using skinless chicken and by not pre-frying vegetables. Some versions call for a fried egg on a slice of fried bread with each portion. This would add 260 calories to an already high 700 calories.

CHICKEN CHASSEUR

Serves 4/240 calories per portion

4 part-boned chicken breasts, 200g/7oz each

5ml/1 teaspoon oil

75g/3oz onion or 2 shallots

200ml/7floz dry white wine

15ml/1 level tablespoon tomato purée

200ml/7floz water

1 chicken stock cube

5ml/1 level teaspoon chopped fresh or 2.5ml/½ level teaspoon dried tarragon

115g/4oz button mushrooms

10ml/2 level teaspoons cornflour

Salt and pepper

Skin the chicken breasts. Brush a non-stick pan with the oil and cook chicken until golden all over. Chop the onion or shallots and add to pan with wine, tomato purée, water, crumbled stock cube and tarragon. Cover and simmer for 25 minutes. Slice the mushrooms and add to pan. Cover and simmer for another 10 minutes: Remove the chicken and keep warm. Mix the cornflour with a little cold water to make a smooth paste, then stir into the pan. Simmer for a few minutes, stirring. Season to taste. Pour over the chicken and serve.

A traditional recipe for this chicken in white wine sauce could cost 640 calories a serving. We cut the cost by discarding the skin from the chicken and using breasts instead of leg joints. Traditionally the vegetables would be pre-fried in fat, but it really isn't necessary to add these extra calories.

CHICKEN PAPRIKA

Serves 4/210 calories per portion

4 chicken breasts, 175g/6oz each

75g/3oz onion

100g/3½oz canned pimento, drained

400g can passata (sieved tomatoes)

15ml/1 level tablespoon paprika

115ml/4floz water

10ml/2 level teaspoons cornflour

150g/5oz low-fat natural yogurt

Discard skin from the chicken breasts and place the breasts in a casserole dish. Finely chop the onion and pimento. Put in a pan with the passata, paprika and water and heat until just boiling. Pour over the chicken. Cover and cook at 170°C/325°F, gas mark 3, for 45 minutes. Mix the cornflour with a little of the yogurt until smooth. Mix in the rest of the yogurt, then stir into the chicken casserole. Cook for another 15 minutes.

Because the skin is discarded from the chicken breasts and they are used instead of unskinned chicken legs, calories are cut by 345 immediately. Then yogurt is used instead of sour cream and no fat is used to cook the vegetables. The saving is 460 calories a portion.

CHICKEN À LA KING

450g/1lb cooked chicken, no skin

50g/2oz lean smoked ham

1 green pepper

115g/4oz mushrooms

10ml/2 teaspoons oil

30ml/2 level tablespoons flour

1 chicken stock cube

275ml/½ pint water

150ml/¼ pint skimmed milk

Salt and pepper

1 to 2 bay leaves

10ml/2 teaspoons dried rosemary

150ml/¼ pint fromage frais, 0% fat

Dice chicken and ham and slice deseeded pepper and mushrooms. Heat the oil in a non-stick pan and sauté pepper and mushrooms for 3-4 minutes. Add the flour and mix thoroughly. Sprinkle in stock cube and gradually stir in water and milk. Add rosemary. Bring to the boil, stirring until thickened. Season and add chicken and ham and heat thoroughly. Stir in fromage frais and serve.

YOU NEED TO ROAST A whole chicken with its skin on as this keeps the flesh moist. But always discard the skin before eating. Traditionally chicken with skin is used for this recipe and would total 975 calories. When you discard the skin and any fat that may remain under the skin, then calories come down to 670 – a saving of 305 calories.

WE HAVE TO ADMIT that the chicken skin does add some flavour to this dish, so we added a little lean smoked ham which gives lots of flavour for just 60 calories.

TRADITIONALLY the vegetables would be sautéed in at least 50g/2oz butter which adds up to 420 calories. Not

only is oil lower in saturated fat, but you can fry with far less. Our Thin Twin recipe uses just 10ml/2 teaspoons oil at 80 calories. That means a saving of 340 calories.

IF YOU BOIL your chicken, then you use the water as stock, any fat from the chicken will go into the stock. So you could end up gaining back quite of a few of the calories you lost by using skinless lean chicken. We used a chicken stock cube for the sauce which costs 30 calories.

INSTEAD of double cream we stirred 0% fat fromage frais into the sauce for another saving of 550 calories

TRADITIONAL RECIPE
Serves 4 at 515 calories per portion

THIN TWIN
Serves 4 at 270 calories per portion

SOLE BONNE FEMME

Serves 4/210 calories per portion

675g/1½lb Dover sole or lemon sole fillets

1 shallot or 25g/1oz onion

115g/4oz button mushrooms

150ml/¼ pint dry white wine

200ml/7floz water

30ml/2 level tablespoons cornflour

30ml/2 level tablespoons skimmed milk powder

50g/2oz fromage frais, 8% fat

Salt and pepper

Fold each fillet of fish into three, tucking the ends underneath with the skin inside. Arrange in a single layer in an ovenproof dish. Chop the shallot or onion and slice the mushrooms and scatter on top. Pour over the wine and water. Cover the dish with a lid or foil and cook in a preheated oven at 180°C/350°F, gas mark 4, for about 15 minutes or until the sole is just cooked. Cover fish and keep warm. Pour the liquid into a pan and boil rapidly, uncovered, until reduced to 225ml/8floz. Mix the cornflour and powdered milk with 50ml/2floz lukewarm water until completely smooth. Whisk into the cooking liquid, then bring to the boil, whisking continuously. Simmer for 2 minutes. Remove from the heat and whisk in the fromage frais. Season to taste with salt and pepper. Pour the sauce over the fish and serve.

A traditional recipe for this fish in wine sauce may call for 65g/2½oz butter (525 calories) and 275ml/½ pint double cream (1,250 calories). We thickened the sauce with cornflour and used skimmed milk powder with fromage frais to give it a creamy taste.

HADDOCK PANCAKES

Serves 4/360 calories per portion

115g/4oz plain flour

575ml/1 pint skimmed milk

2 eggs, size 3

Salt and black pepper

5ml/1 teaspoon oil

450g/1lb smoked haddock

1 bay leaf

1 slice onion

115g/4oz canned or frozen sweetcorn

30ml/2 level tablespoons cornflour

25g/1oz reduced-fat Cheddar cheese

Make a batter with the flour, 275ml/½ pint milk, 1 egg and a pinch salt. Brush a non-stick pan with oil. Make 8 pancakes. Place haddock in a pan with remaining milk, bay leaf and onion. Cover and poach gently for 10 minutes. Strain milk into a measuring jug and make up to 275ml/½ pint with water. Discard bay leaf and onion. Skin, bone and flake fish. Boil frozen sweetcorn. Hard boil remaining egg. Cool, shell and chop. Mix cornflour with a little of the milk. Heat remaining milk until boiling. Pour onto the cornflour, stirring. Return to pan and bring to the boil, stirring. Simmer for 2 minutes. Stir in smoked haddock, sweetcorn, and egg. Season with pepper. Divide the filling between the pancakes and roll up. Arrange in an ovenproof dish. Grate the cheese on top. Bake at 190°C/375°F, gas mark 5, for 15 minutes.

The pancakes are made with skimmed milk and fried in the minimum of oil. The haddock filling is made with a low-fat sauce and reduced-fat Cheddar cheese used instead of high-calorie Cheddar.

PRAWN AND HAM JAMBAYLA

Serves 4/335 calories per portion

1 medium onion
2 sticks celery
1 small green pepper
1 clove garlic
275g/10oz lean cooked ham (preferably sliced ¼-inch thick)
115g/4oz risotto rice
400g/14oz can passata (sieved tomatoes)
175ml/6floz water
1 chicken stock cube
15ml/1 level tablespoon chopped parsley
1.25ml/¼ level teaspoon ground cloves
1.25ml/¼ level teaspoon cayenne pepper
Salt and pepper
225g/8oz prawns

Chop the onion, celery and deseeded pepper. Crush the garlic. Discard all visible fat from ham and cut the lean into small cubes. Place the onion, celery, pepper, garlic and ham in a pan with all the other ingredients except the prawns. Stir well, then bring to the boil. Cover the pan and simmer gently for 25 minutes. Stir frequently and add more water if necessary to prevent sticking. When cooked the mixture should be moist but the excess liquid should all be absorbed. Add the prawns and heat through for a few minutes.

No fat is used to pre-fry the vegetables and rice. Lean ham is used instead of the traditional fatty ham. So you save about 200 calories.

HALIBUT MORNAY

Serves 4/270 calories per portion

4 halibut steaks, 175g/6oz each
1 bay leaf
1 sprig parsley
Lemon slice
275ml/½ pint skimmed milk
30ml/2 level tablespoons cornflour
50g/2oz full flavoured reduced-fat Cheddar cheese
15g/½oz freshly grated Parmesan cheese
Salt, pepper and mustard
25g/1oz fresh wholemeal breadcrumbs

Place halibut steaks in a single layer in an oven-proof dish with the bay leaf, parsley and lemon. Add the milk; cover dish with a lid or foil and cook at 180°C/350°F, gas mark 4, for 20 minues or until the fish is just cooked. Discard the bay leaf, parsley and lemon. Drain off the milk into a measuring jug. Make up to 275ml/½ pint with water if necessary. Mix the cornflour with a little cold water to make a smooth paste. Gradually add the cooking milk, stirring all the time. Return to the pan and bring to the boil, stirring continuously. Simmer for 2 minutes. Grate the Cheddar cheese and add half to sauce with Parmesan cheese. Season with salt, pepper and mustard. Pour over fish and sprinkle the remaining cheese and breadcrumbs on top. Grill until the cheese melts and the crumbs brown.

The traditional recipe calls for full fat milk, butter, flour and about 115g/4oz cheese to make the sauce. So that can add around 140 calories to this otherwise saintly luxurious fish.

FISH PIE

450g/1lb white fish fillet
1 fish stock cube
425ml/¾ pint water
450g/1lb potatoes, peeled weight
225g/8oz swede, peeled weight
1 medium onion
30ml/2 level tablespoons cornflour
25g/1oz skimmed milk powder
115g/4oz peeled prawns
115g/4oz frozen peas
30ml/2 tablespoons skimmed milk

Poach fish in a pan with stock cube and water. Simmer gently until the fish flakes easily (approximately 15 minutes). Boil potatoes and swede until tender. Strain liquid from the fish, make up to 425ml/¾ pint with extra water if necessary. Discard any skin and bones from fish, then flake the fish. Chop onion. Blend fish stock with cornflour and skimmed milk powder. Bring to the boil, stirring all the time. Stir in the fish, onion, prawns and peas. Place in an ovenproof dish. Mash the drained potato and swede together with the skimmed milk. Spread or pipe over the fish. Cook the pie at 200°C/400°F, gas mark 6, for 40 minutes.

WHITE FISH, plain and unadorned, is a low-calorie slimming friend. It's a rich sauce that sends calories sky high. Traditional fish pie, with its creamy sauce and buttery mash topping, is no exception – soaring to around 680 calories per portion! But not if you make your fish pie the Thin Twin way. Our delicious version makes an ideal family meal, yet cuts the portion cost to just 300 calories.

TRADITIONAL FISH PIE relies on butter, full-cream milk and the odd dollop of cream for its rich smooth flavour. We said a firm no to these high-calorie ingredients. For every 28g/1oz butter you omit from a recipe you save 210 calories and a traditional fish pie would contain at least 50g/2oz. Cutting out just 30ml/2 tablespoons single cream would save 60 calories. Our basic sauce is thickened with cornflour (not the usual roux of butter and flour). Instead of poaching the fish in full fat milk, we used fish stock, later adding skimmed milk powder. That knocked 285 calories from the recipe's total.

AN EXTRA-ZESTY potato topping comes from mixing traditional mash with mashed swede instead of egg and butter. Swede costs just 6 calories for 28g/1oz compared to potatoes' 25 calories. So this swap saves 140 calories. Not adding 1 egg and 28g/1oz butter to the mash topping saves another 290 calories.

THE RESULT IS A DISH that doesn't taste low-calorie at all! Add green vegetables or grilled tomatoes, and you have a satisfying family main meal for under 400 calories per portion. Enjoy it!

TRADITIONAL RECIPE
Serves 4 at 670 calories per portion

THIN TWIN
Serves 4 at 300 calories per portion

DESSERTS
AND CAKES

Ask any slimmer what is the hardest food to resist when eating out and she is likely to say it is a luscious looking dessert. In this chapter are some mouthwatering recipes that would look good on any sweet trolley, which taste every bit as good as they look, but are nicely low in calories.

Even old traditional favourites such as Bread and Butter Pudding and Bakewell Tart have had their calories sliced in half and no single serving of any of the desserts or cakes goes above 270 calories – many are far lower than this.

When planning a meal when you are dieting, it is best to decide before you start what you are going to eat and how many calories that will add up to. And if a dessert is what you desire most, then there is no point in thinking that you will eat a starter followed by a main couse and then be able to resist sampling that sweet temptation.

Be realistic and miss the course you least crave. Or cut down the amount you eat so that you can indulge in a pud. But don't, on the other hand, eat a dessert just because you have got into the habit of a sweet ending to a meal. For a minimum calorie cost you could have a piece of fruit or a very-low-calorie diet fromage frais or yogurt. Or just have a spoonful off someone else's plate – if they are agreeable, of course!

If you are stewing fruit for dessert, you can save literally hundreds of calories by using a low-calorie sweetener instead of sugar. For example you would normally use 50g/2oz sugar to sweeten 225g/8oz rhubarb. If you used a liquid low calorie sweetener instead - add after cooking -

then you would save 210 calories.

By the way, if you still think that biscuits and cheese are a low-calorie ending to a meal, think again. Three small crackers and a hunk of cheese could add up to 325 calories or more. Ordinary Cheddar is 117 calories an ounce and most people would cut at least a 50g/2oz slice. If you served up a reduced-fat Cheddar you could make a Thin Twin version of biscuits and cheese which would save you about 75 calories for three crackers and 50g/2oz Cheddar. But don't spread your crackers first with butter unless you want to add 105 calories for half an ounce.

If you have a very sweet tooth, it is worth while trying to retrain yourself to like less sweet things – yes, it is possible! Many a slimmer who has persevered with this says they could never go back to eating the very sugary items they once tucked into with great relish. When you use less sugar, it often allows more flavour to come through from other ingredients, such as fruit, and although we have reduced the amount of sugar in our Thin Twin recipes – mostly using fructose the fruit sugar instead of sucrose – we hope you will agree that the recipes are no less delicious because of this. Try them and see.

TRIFLE

4 trifle sponges

20ml/4 level teaspoons reduced-sugar jam

30ml/2 tablespoons sweet sherry

1 packet Birds sugar-free jelly

411g/14½oz can apricots or peaches in natural juice

450ml/¾ pint skimmed milk

45ml/3 level tablespoons custard powder

20ml/4 level teaspoons fructose

150ml/¼ pint reduced-fat double cream alternative

Nectarine or peach, kiwi fruit and strawberries

Split sponges and spread with jam. Place in a glass bowl. Drain fruit, reserving the juice. Mix 45ml/3 tablespoons juice with sherry and sprinkle over sponges. Arrange fruit around sponges. Make up jelly, using reserved juice to replace part of the water. Leave until it starts to gel, then pour over sponges. Chill until set. Put custard powder, fructose and a little milk in bowl and make a smooth paste. Heat remaining milk, then stir into custard paste. Return to pan and bring to boil, stirring continuously. Simmer until it thickens. Pour into a basin and cover with damp greaseproof paper to prevent a skin forming. When custard is cool, spread over jelly. Whip cream alternative until thick, then spread or pipe over the custard. Decorate with fresh fruit.

WE USED a reduced-sugar jam which tastes fruitier and fresher than the ordinary sort. The saving is just 20 calories for 4 level teaspoons but little savings can mount up.

ORDINARY JELLIES are surprisingly high in calories (340 for the usual 575ml/1 pint). We used a sugar-free jelly and saved 290 calories.

APRICOTS OR PEACHES in syrup would cost about 300 for a 411g/14½oz can. Natural juice lets the fruity flavour come through and saves about 110 calories.

FRUCTOSE, the fruit sugar in powder form, costs just 7 fewer calories per ounce than sugar (sucrose). But it is much sweeter so you can use less. It is ideal for custards and gives a saving of 100 calories for our trifle.

SILVER TOP MILK costs 380 calories a pint. Skimmed milk a mere 195! And as skimmed milk makes a very good custard, with a saving here of 140 calories, then it's a swap well worth making.

NO TRIFLE can do without its cream, but double cream costs a wicked 635 calories per 150ml/¼ pint. Shape Double and Delight Double Cream Alternative are cream substitutes which give a saving of 280 calories.

THE TRADITIONAL decoration of glacé cherries, flaked almonds and angelica can easily add over 250 sneaky calories. Fresh fruit looks just as enticingly pretty and would hardly make a dent in a calorie allowance.

TRADITIONAL RECIPE
Serves 6 at 415 calories per portion

THIN TWIN RECIPE
Serves 6 at 230 calories per portion

BANANA FOOL

Serves 6/90 calories per portion

2 medium bananas

Juice of 1 lemon

15ml/1 level tablespoon honey

275ml/½ pint skimmed milk

30ml/2 level tablespoons fructose

30ml/2 level tablespoons custard powder

60ml/4 level tablespoons fromage frais, 8% fat

Purée peeled bananas with lemon juice until smooth. Stir in honey. Mix 45ml/3 tablespoons milk with the fructose and custard powder until smooth. Heat remaining milk in a pan until on the point of boiling, remove from the heat and pour over the custard. Stir well and return to the pan. Stir over a low heat until the custard thickens. Remove from the heat and leave to cool slightly. Stir in the bananas and fromage frais, then spoon the fool into serving glasses. Chill before serving. Eat within 1½ hours of making.

The custard is usually made with full fat milk and cream would be added, too. We've used skimmed milk and fromage frais and replaced sugar with far less fructose and honey. Result: a dessert that would fool anyone into thinking it is high in calories costing over 100 fewer calories than its 'fat twin.'

RASPBERRY SOUFFLÉ

Serves 8/150 calories

10ml/2 teaspoons oil

450g/1lb raspberries

4 eggs, size 3

70g/2½oz fructose

30ml/2 level tablespoons gelatine

75ml/5 tablespoons unsweetened orange juice

275g/10oz fromage frais, 8% fat

Tie a band of double greaseproof paper around a 1 litre/¾ pint soufflé dish to stand 2 inches above the rim. Oil the inside. Purée the raspberries and sieve to remove the pips. Separate the eggs and place the yolks in a bowl with the fructose and whisk with an electric mixer until thick and creamy in colour. Put gelatine in a small bowl with the orange juice and dissolve over a pan of hot water. Add to the purée. Carefully fold into the egg and fructose mixture with the fromage frais. Whisk the whites until stiff and fold into the soufflé. Spoon into the soufflé dish and chill for 3 to 4 hours. Remove the collar of greaseproof paper and decorate soufflé with the remaining raspberries.

To cut calories by almost half (a normal serving would be 280 calories), fructose replaces sugar, and the biggest saving comes from substituting fromage frais for calorie-laden double cream.

CHILLED LEMON CHEESECAKE

Serves 8/185 calories per serving

10ml/2 teaspoons oil

75g/3oz digestive biscuits

40g/1½oz low-fat spread

2 eggs, size 3

1 sachet gelatine

115g/4oz skimmed milk soft cheese

115g/4oz curd cheese

60ml/4 level tablespoons fromage frais, 8% fat

50g/2oz fructose

15ml/1 level tablespoon honey

2 lemons

Grease a 20cm/8inch loose-bottomed tin with oil. Crush biscuits and mix with melted low-fat spread. Press into the base of the tin and chill for 10 minutes. Separate eggs (only 1 yolk is needed). Put gelatine in a small bowl with 45ml/3 tablespoons water and dissolve over a pan of hot water. Mix together cheeses, fromage frais, fructose, yolk, honey and the juice and grated rind of lemons . Whisk egg whites until they form soft peaks and fold into the mixture. Stir in the gelatine and spoon mixture into the tin, Chill for 2 to 3 hours before turning out the cheesecake onto a serving dish.

Butter is usually used to bind the biscuits and full-fat soft cheese instead of skimmed milk low-fat cheese. Double cream also figures a great deal in traditional recipes. All in all our Thin Twin costs 200 calories a portion less than a traditional lemon cheesecake and still has a deliciously creamy taste.

PLUM MOUSSE

Serves 6/110 calories per portion

450g/1lb ripe plums, stoned

75ml/5 tablespoons water

50g/2oz fructose

120ml/8 level tablespoons fromage frais, 8% fat

175g/6oz skimmed milk soft cheese

1 sachet gelatine

Place plums in a pan with 30ml/2 tablespoons water and bring to the boil. Reduce the heat and simmer for 6 to 8 minutes until the plums are tender. Remove from the heat, cool slightly, then purée. Stir in fructose. Mix fromage frais with the soft cheese until well blended, then stir in the plum purée. Put gelatine in a small bowl with 45ml/3 tablespoons water and dissolve over a pan of hot water. Stir into the mousse. Spoon mousse into glasses and chill for 3 hours until set.

Double cream is a terrifically high 125 calories an ounce and you could usually be asked to add about 275g/10oz to a fruit mousse. That adds up to 1,250 calories! When you blend fromage frais with skimmed milk soft cheese you get the texture and taste of cream and the amount we've used in this Thin Twin adds up to just 270 calories.

STRAWBERRY CHEESECAKE

75g/3oz digestive biscuits

40g/1½oz low-fat spread

15g/½oz gelatine

45ml/3 tablespoons water

350g/12oz skimmed milk soft cheese

2 small cartons strawberry diet yogurt

Low-calorie sweetener (optional)

2 egg whites

1 kiwi fruit

50g/2oz strawberries

Crush the biscuits. Melt the low-fat spread and mix with biscuit crumbs. Press into base of an 18-20cm/7-8 inch loose-base tin. Chill until firm. Put gelatine in a small bowl with water and dissolve over a pan of hot water. Allow to cool. Stir yogurt into cheese and mix well. Add sweetener to taste. Stir in gelatine. Whisk egg whites until stiff. Fold into cheese mixture and pour onto base. Chill until set. Decorate with sliced kiwi fruit and strawberries.

SADLY A LOW-CALORIE biscuit is still a product of the future, but we used fewer biscuits than a traditional recipe would call for and although the base is thinner our Thin Twin still has the taste and texture that makes cheesecakes extra special.

WE CUT OUT BUTTER and substituted low-fat spread to mix with the biscuit crumbs. Low-fat spread is half the calories of butter and this saved 160 calories.

ANY CLASSIC cheesecake recipe would tell you to take cream cheese at 125 calories for 25g/1oz and blend it with double cream at exactly the same calorie cost. We used skimmed milk soft cheese which saves 300 calories. And we blended this with very-low-fat yogurts which saves an enormous 1,120 calories more.

FRESH FRUIT dresses the top of our cheesecake in an attractive way and cost very few calories. A traditional cheesecake may well have double cream piped on top, too, and add up to 515 calories a portion.

THIN TWIN
Serves 6 at 190 calories per portion

TRADITIONAL RECIPE
Serves 6 at 515 calories per portion

GOOSEBERRY FOOL

Serves 4/110 calories per portion

450g/1lb gooseberries, topped and tailed

25g/1oz fructose (fruit sugar)

15ml/1 level tablespoon custard powder

150ml/¼ pint skimmed milk

3 x 125g dieter's gooseberry yogurts

Place the gooseberries in a pan with 4 tablespoons water, then cover and cook for 15 minutes. Cool for 10 minutes and then stir in fructose. Place gooseberries in a blender or food processor and purée. Blend the custard powder with a little of the milk. Heat the remaining milk in a pan and pour over the custard powder, then return to pan and stir over a gentle heat until thickened. Beat the custard into the fruit purée and allow to cool before stirring in the yogurts. Pour the fool into individual serving dishes and chill before serving.

Skimmed milk is used instead of whole milk, very-low-fat yogurts instead of double cream. We also added fructose instead of sugar and only used a quarter of the quantity a classic fool contains as the yogurts add some sweetness, too. The saving is almost 200 calories a portion.

RHUBARB CHIFFON PIE

Serves 8/165 calories per portion

10ml/2 teaspoons oil

75g/3oz digestive biscuits

40g/1½oz low-fat spread

450g/1lb rhubarb, trimmed

90ml/6 tablespoons water

1 orange

2 eggs, size 3

75g/3oz fructose

30ml/2 level tablespoons cornflour

2.5ml/½ level teaspoon ginger

1 sachet gelatine

Grease a 20cm/8 inch cake tin with the oil. Crush biscuits and mix with the melted low-fat spread. Press into the base of the tin and chill. Place rhubarb in a pan with 60ml/4 tablespoons water and bring to the boil. Simmer for 5 minutes until soft, but still holding its shape. Cool slightly, then purée and stir in 25g/1oz fructose. Set to one side. Place grated rind and juice of orange in a pan. Separate eggs and add yolks, remaining fructose, cornflour and ginger. Heat gently, stirring, until thick, then stir in rhubarb. Put gelatine in small bowl with remaining water and dissolve over a pan of hot water. Whisk egg whites until stiff and fold into custard with the gelatine. Spoon onto the biscuit base and chill for 4 hours or until set.

We mixed a smaller amount of digestive biscuits with low-fat spread rather than butter. And we cut a whole lot of sugar from this delicious dessert. A classic recipe would ask you to add 75g/3oz sugar to the base, another 75g/3oz to the rhubarb and the same amount to the custard. That means a traditional recipe could add up to 300 calories a portion.

EVE'S PUDDING

Serves 8/200 calories per portion

450g/1lb cooking apples, peeled and cored weight

30ml/2 tablespoons water

100g/3½oz fructose (fruit sugar)

½ a lemon

115g/4oz low-fat spread

150g/5oz self-raising flour

2 eggs, size 3

Cut the apple into bite-sized pieces and place in a 1.2 litre/2 pint ovenproof dish with the water, grated rind of lemon and juice and 40g/1½oz fructose. Cream together the low-fat spread and the remaining fructose until pale and fluffy and beat in the eggs gradually. Fold in the flour and the mixture should now resemble a firm dropping consistency. Spoon the cake mixture onto the apples and spread evenly. Bake at 190°C/375°F, gas mark 5, for 40 minutes or until golden brown and the sponge is well risen. Serve hot.

> The apples are normally sweetened with far more sugar. But what would really bump up the calories in this popular pud's bottom layer would be the 175g/6oz butter that would be added to the apples, too.
> Butter would usually be used in the sponge and icing sugar sprinkled on after baking. So a classic Eve's Pudding could add up to 450 calories a portion.

APPLE AND BERRY COBBLER

Serves 8/180 calories per portion

450g/1lb cooking apples, peeled and cored weight

225g/8oz blackberries or raspberries, fresh or frozen

45ml/3 tablespoons water

75g/3oz fructose (fruit sugar)

225g/8oz plain flour

Pinch salt

10ml/2 level teaspoons cinnamon

15ml/1 level tablespoon baking powder

40g/1½oz low-fat spread (suitable for baking)

150ml/¼ pint skimmed milk

Slice apples and place in a pan with berries and water. Cover and cook over a low heat for 15 minutes or until apples are tender. Cool, then stir in 50g/2oz fructose. Spoon into an ovenproof dish and set to one side. Sieve flour, salt, cinnamon and baking powder into a bowl and rub in the spread until the mixture resembles breadcrumbs. Add the remaining fructose and stir in milk to form a soft dough. Sprinkle 30ml/2 tablespoons extra flour on a work surface and roll dough until ¾inch thick. Cut out 16 rounds 2inch in diameter. Place in an overlapping pattern over the fruit and bake at 180°C/350°F, gas mark 4, for 20-25 minutes or until the scones are golden brown on top.

> Fructose is much sweeter than sugar, so we've used far less than a traditional recipe would require. The scone would be made with at least 115g/4oz butter and full cream milk. The fat twin of this pud would be at least 400 calories a serving.

BAKEWELL TART

200g/7oz self-raising flour plus I5ml/1 level tablespoon

115g/4oz low-fat spread suitable for baking

45ml/3 level tablespoons reduced-sugar morello cherry jam

25g/1oz fructose (fruit sugar)

1 egg, size 3

45ml/3 level tablespoons ground almonds

Few drops almond essence

30ml/2 level tablespoons icing sugar

Sieve 150g/5oz flour into a bowl and rub in 50g/2oz low-fat spread until the mixture resembles breadcrumbs. Add enough water to make a soft dough. Use 15ml/1 level tablespoon flour sprinkled on surface, roll out pastry to 18cm/7 inch circle and use to line a flan dish. Prick the pastry and bake at 170˚C/325˚F, gas mark 3, for 10 minutes. Allow to cool slightly then spread with the warmed jam. Cream the remaining spread with the fructose and add the egg and beat well. Fold in the remaining flour, ground almonds and essence. Spoon onto the jam and bake at 180˚C/350˚F, gas mark 4, for 25 minutes or untı, golden brown. Mix the icing sugar with 30ml/2 tablespoons water and spread over Bakewell Tart while still warm.

THE OLD-STYLE cookery books always tell you to grease the dish when you bake pastry. But this really is unneccessary. And because the fat will be absorbed by the tart, it can add over 80 calories to your recipe.

A RICH PASTRY BASE makes the bottom of a Bakewell Tart very calorie costly. We used low-fat spread instead of butter and omitted the egg and sugar that would usually be added.

THE JAM THAT is spread over the pastry case could add up to 225 calories. We used reduced-sugar jam and we cut the amount by 30ml/2 tablespoons. That saves 150 calories.

GROUND ALMONDS are a necessary ingredient, but like all nuts they are high in calories. A traditional recipe would call for 50g/2oz costing 240 calories. Our Thin Twin uses just 75ml/3 level tablespoons ground almonds and enhances the flavour with almond essence. The flour is increased to provide bulk , but that still gives a saving of 80 calories.

WE SAVED LOTS more calories by using low-fat spread instead of butter and a reduced amount of fructose instead of sugar (saving 320 calories). A little whole milk is also normally added which isn't necessary in the Thin Twin version, and gives an extra saving of 40 calories.

IN TOTAL we cut 1,380 calories from a traditional Bakewell Tart recipe. And we guarantee that everyone you serve this to will say it's a classy creation.

TRADITIONAL RECIPE
Serves 6 at 500 calories per portion
THIN TWIN
Serves 6 at 270 calories per portion

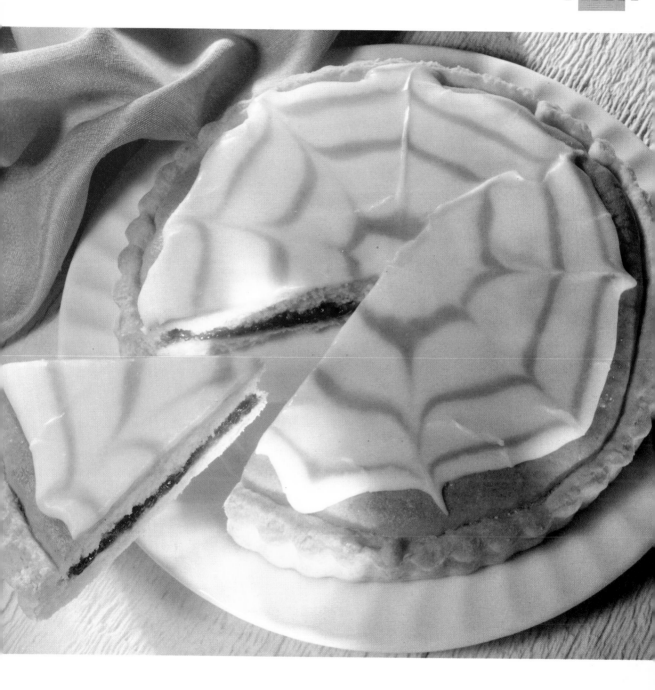

APPLE STRUDEL

Serves 6/200 calories per slice

275g/10oz cooking apples, peeled weight

60ml/4 tablespoons water

50g/2oz fructose (fruit sugar)

50g/2oz raisins

Grated rind of 1 lemon

10ml/2 level teaspoons cinnamon

175g/6oz filo pastry (6 sheets)

15ml/1 tablespoon oil

30ml/2 level tablespoons chopped mixed nuts

Cut apple into bite-sized pieces and place in a pan with the water. Bring to the boil, reduce the heat and simmer for 10 minutes. Stir in the fructose, raisins, lemon rind and cinnamon and allow to cool slightly. Place 3 sheets of the filo pastry on a baking tray lightly greased with some of the oil and add the apple filling. Spread out evenly over the pastry, leaving a 1-inch space around the edges. Add the remaining pastry and brush with the oil. Sprinkle over the nuts and bake at 200°C/400°F, gas mark 6, for 25 minutes until the pastry is golden brown. Cut into 6 slices and serve.

> **A traditional version of this Austrian dessert would have butter added to the apples, about twice as much sugar as fructose, and nuts added to the filling. The pastry would be richer, too. With our Thin Twin we've managed to trim down calories by 250 a portion.**

PASSION CAKE

Serves 8/215 calories per portion

10ml/2 teaspoons oil

175g/6oz carrots, peeled weight

50g/2oz fructose

115g/4oz low-fat spread

2 eggs, size 3

150g/5oz self-raising flour

10ml/2 teaspoons cinnamon

50g/2oz raisins

50g/2oz skimmed milk soft cheese

45ml/3 tablespoons orange juice

30ml/2 tablespoons chopped nuts

Grease a 20cm/8inch cake tin with oil. Finely grate carrots. Cream together the fructose and low-fat spread until pale and fluffy. Beat in the eggs one at a time, then gradually fold in the flour and cinnamon with carrots and raisins. Spoon into the cake tin and bake at 190°C/375°F, gas mark 5, for 30 minutes or until golden brown on the surface. Cool before turning out. Mix together the skimmed milk soft cheese and orange juice and spread over top of cake. Sprinkle over the nuts and divide into 8 pieces before serving.

> **We've swapped butter for low-fat spread and sugar for fructose. We cut out walnuts from the filling and used raisins which add to the sweetness, too. Traditionally the topping is made with full fat soft cheese and far more nuts are sprinkled on top. All in all we saved 185 calories a portion.**

BANANA BREAD

Serves 8/185 calories per slice

10ml/2 teaspoons oil

115g/4oz low-fat spread

50g/2oz fructose

2 eggs, size 3

115g/4oz wholemeal self-raising flour

2 small bananas

25g/1oz walnuts

Grease a 575ml/1 pint loaf tin with the oil. Cream together the low-fat spread and fructose until light and fluffy, then beat in the eggs. Fold in the flour, mashed bananas and walnuts, then mix thoroughly. Spoon into the loaf tin and bake at 180°C/350°F, gas mark 4, for 40 minutes or until firm to the touch and golden brown. Cool before turning out onto a serving dish and cutting into 8 slices.

In this Thin Twin we've cut a slice of this traditional teatime treat by a whole 260 calories. The Thin Twin uses low-fat spread instead of butter, fructose instead of brown sugar, wholemeal flour and about a third of the amount of very high-calorie walnuts. The result is a moist bread which you won't need to spread with butter either.

BLUEBERRY MUFFINS

Makes 14/100 calories per muffin

15ml/1 teaspoon oil

50g/2oz oat bran

200ml/7floz skimmed milk

25g/1oz butter or margarine

50g/2oz fructose

1 egg, size 3

115g/4oz plain flour

2.5ml/½ teaspoon salt

15ml/1 level tablespoon baking powder

150g/5oz blueberries

Grease individual patty tins with oil. Preheat the oven to 190°C/375°F, gas mark 5. Place the bran and milk in a bowl and leave to soak for 5 minutes. Melt the butter or margarine. Remove from the heat and stir in the fructose and the bran mixture. Lightly beat the egg. Sieve together the flour, salt and baking powder and add the blueberries. Make a well in the centre and pour in the bran mixture with the egg. Mix together until evenly blended. Divide between the patty tins and bake for 20 to 25 minutes until firm and golden brown on top.

Our recipe replaces full cream milk and sugar with skimmed milk and fructose – making an immediate saving of 450 calories. We've used less flour – and therefore less fat – and kept in moisture by adding milk-soaked oat bran. Our muffins cut calories by virtually half – 100 calories each as against 190.

FRENCH APPLE TART

115g/4oz self-raising flour, plus 15ml/1 level tablespoon

57g/2¼oz low-fat spread

22g/¾oz butter or margarine

5ml/1 level teaspoon sugar

25ml/5 teaspoons water

1kg/2lb cooking apples

60ml/4 level tablespoons reduced-sugar apricot jam

Finely grated rind of ½ lemon

225g/8oz eating apples

30ml/2 tablespoons lemon juice

Sieve 115g/4oz flour into a bowl and rub in 32g/1¼oz low-fat spread and the butter or margarine until the mixture resembles fine breadcrumbs. Stir in sugar; add the water and bind together. Roll the pastry out thinly on a floured surface. Line a 210cm/8¼inch flan ring with pastry. Prick the base a number of times and bake at 170°C/325°F, gas mark 3, for 10 minutes. Peel cooking apples, discard cores and roughly chop flesh. Melt remaining low-fat spread in a pan and add the apples with 30ml/2 tablespoons water. Cover and cook gently for 15 minutes until the apples are soft. Blend the mixture until smooth and add 45ml/3 level tablespoons of apricot jam and the lemon rind. Return apple purée to pan and cook for 15 minutes, stirring occasionally, until thickened. Spoon purée into the flan case and allow to cool. Slice eating apples, discard cores, and arrange in an overlapping pattern on apple purée. Brush with lemon juice and bake at 200°C/400°F, gas mark 6, for 25 minutes, until the apples are lightly coloured. Gently warm remaining jam and brush over top of the flan. Serve hot or cold.

A TRADITIONAL pastry case calls for egg and butter. We left out the egg. We cut the butter down and mixed it with low-fat spread. That gave a saving of 335 calories.

THE APPLE PURÉE filling is usually a rich mix of cooking apples with butter, caster sugar and apricot jam which totals 825 calories! Because we used eating apples (Cox's are best) for the topping it meant we could cut out the sugar from the apple purée saving 225 calories.

INSTEAD OF butter we mixed half the amount of low-fat spread into the purée – quite enough to give the desired creamy texture, with a saving of 310 calories.

A REDUCED-SUGAR JAM not only gives a worthwhile calorie saving, but it also tastes fruitier. The amount we added gave our purée a delicate apricot flavour and saved 110 calories!

THE SLICED APPLE topping is traditionally made with tartish French apples, dusted over with 25g/1oz sugar. We used sweet apples and saved 110 sugary calories.

FINISHING TOUCH. The apricot jam glaze: instead of of apricot jam we brushed on a little reduced-sugar jam and saved 25 calories!

TRADITIONAL RECIPE
Serves 6 at 445 calories per portion

THIN TWIN
Serves 6 at 240 calories per portion

STRAWBERRY ICE CREAM

Serves 8/110 calories per portion

450g/1lb strawberries
75g/3oz fructose
225g/8oz fromage frais, 8% fat
175g/6oz skimmed milk soft cheese
4 egg whites, size 3

Purée strawberries in a liquidizer or blender and sieve to remove the pips (optional). Stir fructose into purée with fromage frais and soft cheese and mix thoroughly until it forms a smooth consistency. Whisk egg whites until stiff and carefully fold into purée. Spoon into a freezerproof container and freeze for 1½ hours. Remove from the freezer and mix the ice cream thoroughly with a hand mixer to break up the frozen pieces (this prevents the ice cream crystallizing). Return to the freezer for a further ½ hour and repeat the mixing process again before allowing the ice cream to fully freeze (approximately 4 hours). Remove from the freezer 1-1½ hours before required to soften.

We've used fructose instead of sugar and a combination of skimmed milk soft cheese and fromage frais instead of cream. Result – a delicious ice cream which saves about 210 calories a portion.

CHERRY ICE CREAM

Serves 8/115 calories per portion

450g/1lb black cherries
50g/2oz fructose
4 cartons diet yogurt, black cherry
90ml/6 level tablespoons fromage frais, 8% fat
75ml/5 level tablespoons ground almonds
2 egg whites, size 3

Halve and stone cherries. Mix together fructose, yogurts, fromage frais and ground almonds and add the cherries. Mix thoroughly to incorporate all the ingredients. Whisk the egg whites until stiff and fold carefully into the mixture. Freeze for at least 4 hours. Remove from freezer 1 hour before serving to soften. One portion will weigh 75g/3oz

Black cherries normally need to have quite a lot of sugar added to them to make a sweet ice cream. We used a smaller amount of fructose and the diet yogurts add sweetness, too. We used yogurt and fromage frais instead of double cream and reduced the amount of ground almonds. Saving is 155 calories a portion.

BROWN BREAD
ICE CREAM

Serves 8/120 calories per portion

150g/5oz wholemeal breadcrumbs
40g/1½oz brown sugar
425g can low-fat ready-made custard
90ml/6 level tablespoons Greek yogurt
1 lemon
2 egg whites, size 3

Place the breadcrumbs and sugar on a baking tray and bake at 200°C/400°F, gas mark 6, for 20 minutes, turning twice to brown and caramelize the breadcrumbs evenly. Mix together custard and yogurt until well blended. Add the juice and grated rind of the lemon, mix well. Stir in the breadcrumbs. Whisk egg whites until stiff and carefully fold into the mixture. Spoon into a freezer container and freeze for 1½ hours. Remove from the freezer and mix thoroughly. Return to the freezer for at least 4 hours. Remove ice cream from the freezer at least 1 hour before serving to allow it to soften. An eighth portion will weigh 75g/3oz.

> You do need to use sugar in this recipe because of its caramelizing properties. But we have used far less than a traditional recipe would require. We have also replaced double cream with low-fat custard and yogurt. You save about 200 calories a portion making this delicious ice cream the Thin Twin way.

APRICOT
ICE CREAM

Serves 8/120 calories per portion

12 ripe apricots, weighing about 65g/2½oz each
25g/1oz fructose
2 cartons Greek yogurt with apricot, 150g each
120ml/8 level tablespoons fromage frais, 8% fat
2 egg whites, size 3

Halve the apricots and remove stones. Purée in a liquidizer or blender until smooth. Stir in the fructose, yogurt and fromage frais and mix thoroughly. Whisk egg whites until stiff and fold into the apricot mixture. Spoon into a freezer container and freeze for 1½ hours. Remove from freezer and mix thoroughly to incorporate all the frozen parts and to prevent the ice cream becoming crystallized. Return to the freezer for at least 4 hours. Remove ice cream from freezer for 1 hour before serving to allow it to soften slightly. A portion will weigh approximately 75g/3oz.

> Yogurt and fromage frais replace double cream and fructose replaces sugar. The result is a delicious fruity ice cream that costs 120 calories a serving instead of the usual 300 calories.

BREAD AND BUTTER PUDDING

150g/5oz medium-sliced white bread, crusts removed

75g/3oz ready-to-eat dried apricots

25g/1oz low-fat spread

30ml/2 level tablespoons reduced-sugar apricot jam

575ml/1 pint skimmed milk

1 vanilla pod

30ml/2 level tablespoons fructose

2 eggs, size 3

Cut each slice of bread into four triangles. Finely chop apricots. Spread one side of each triangle with low-fat spread and the other with apricot jam. Arrange half the bread, spread side down, in an ovenproof dish. Sprinkle with half the apricots. Add remaining bread triangles and top with remaining apricots. Place milk with vanilla pod in pan and bring almost to boiling point. Remove from heat and leave to stand for 10 minutes. Then add the fructose and beaten eggs and mix well. Strain and pour over the bread and apricots. Allow to stand for 30 minutes so that some of the milk is absorbed by the bread. Place dish in a baking tray which is half filled with boiling water and bake at 170°C/325°F, gas mark 3, for 45 minutes or until golden brown.

HOW WERE calories cut ? The 75g/3oz butter that classic recipes call for costs an astronomic 630 calories! Just 25g/1oz low-fat spread (110 calories) goes on so easily that it's quite enough to cover the bread and give a big saving of 520 calories.

FRUCTOSE is around three times sweeter than sugar; so we used 2 level tablespoons, weighing only 20g/¾oz, and costing a mere 80 calories. Extra sweetness comes from fruity, reduced-sugar apricot jam costing just 50 calories.

TRADITIONAL RECIPES add at least 50g/2oz currants or sultanas. We saved 20 calories and give our Thin Twin recipe an extra fruity flavour and bulk by adding 75g/3oz ready-to-eat dried apricots instead.

YOU MIGHT THINK that full cream milk is essential to give the necessary rich texture; but a vanilla pod added to a pint of skimmed milk gives a taste of real luxury plus a saving of 190 calories. Alternatively you could use a few drops of vanilla essence for no extra calories.

NO NEED TO USE the traditional two size-2 eggs, at 180 calories. Size 3 gives the same rich smoothness and saves a further 20 calories.

WE CUT THE AMOUNT of bread from the usual 175g/6oz to 150g/5oz – this saves 65 calories.

LUXURY VARIETIES of bread and butter pudding add around 150ml/¼ pint single cream and 280 extra calories. We wouldn't dream of doing such a thing; and the lovely flavour and texture of our Thin Twin pudding makes it quite unnecessary.

TRADITIONAL RECIPE
Serves 4 at 500 calories per portion

THIN TWIN
Serves 4 at 260 calories per portion

CHART OF BASIC FOODS

Below you will find the calories in most basic foods. Use these to select accompaniments to Thin Twin meals

A

ABALONE

Canned, drained, per 28g/1oz	41

ACKEE

Canned, drained, per 28g/1oz	43

AGAR

Dried, per 28g/1oz	90

ALFALFA SPROUTS

Per 28g/1oz	10

ALMONDS

Shelled, per 28g/1oz	160
Flaked, per 15ml/1 level tablespoon	35
Ground, per 15ml/1 level tablespoon	40
Per almond, whole	10
Per sugared almond	15

ANCHOVIES

Canned, drained, per 28g/1oz	40
Per anchovy fillet	5
Per 50g average can, drained	55

ANCHOVY ESSENCE

Per 5ml/1 level teaspoon	5

ANGELICA

Per 28g/1oz	90

APPLES

Per 28g/1oz unless otherwise stated

Cooking, flesh only	11
Dried apple rings	65
Eating, flesh only	13
Eating, whole	10
Medium whole eating, 142g/5oz	50
Medium whole cooking, 227g/8oz	80
Apple juice, per 28ml/1floz	11
Concentrated Apple Juice, per 28ml/1floz	63
Apple sauce, sweetened, per 15ml/1 level tablespoon	20
Apple sauce, unsweetened, per 15ml/1 level tablespoon	10

APRICOTS

Per 28g/1oz unless otherwise stated

Canned in natural juice	13
Canned in syrup	30
Dried	52
Fresh with stone	7
Hunza, per dried apricot	10
Hunza, stewed, drained without stones	21
No-need-to-soak variety	40
Per dried apricot	10
Per apricot half, canned in syrup, drained	15
Per apricot half, canned in natural juice, drained	5
Per whole fresh fruit	10

ARROWROOT

Per 28g/1oz	101
Per 5ml/1 level teaspoon	10

ARTICHOKES

Globe, boiled, per 28g/1oz	4
1 medium globe artichoke	10
Jerusalem, raw, unpeeled, per 28g/1oz	7
Jerusalem, boiled, per 28g/1oz	5

ASPARAGUS

Raw or boiled, soft tips, per 28g/1oz	5
Per asparagus spear	5

AUBERGINES (EGG PLANTS)

Raw, per 28g/1oz	4
Sliced, fried, 28g/1oz raw weight	60
Whole aubergine, 198g/7oz	30

AVOCADO

Flesh only, per 28g/1oz	63
Per medium half avocado, 57g/2oz	125

B

BABACO

Whole fruit with skin, seeds removed	195
Flesh only, per 28g/1oz	12

BACON

Per 28g/1oz unless otherwise stated

Back rashers, trimmed, rind removed, raw	65
Back rashers, trimmed, well grilled	80
Collar rashers, rind on, raw	75
Collar rashers, rind on, well grilled	80
Middle rashers, rind removed, raw	80
Middle rashers, rind removed, well grilled	75
Streaky rashers, rind removed, raw	85
Streaky rashers, rind removed, well grilled	110
1 back rasher, trimmed, well grilled, 28g/1oz raw weight	40
1 bacon chop, 85g/3oz raw, well grilled	125
1 middle rasher, rind removed, well grilled, 45g/1¾oz raw weight	65
1 round bacon steak, well grilled, 99g/3½oz raw weight	105
1 streaky rasher, rind removed, well grilled, 28g/1oz raw weight	50

BAKING POWDER

Per 28g/1oz	46
Per 5ml/1 level teaspoon	5

BAMBOO SHOOTS

Canned, per 28g/1oz	5

BANANAS

Banana Chips, per 28g/1oz	147
Flesh only, per 28g/1oz	22
Flesh and skin, per 28g/1oz	13
Small whole fruit, 113g/4oz	55
Medium whole fruit, 170g/6oz	80
Large whole fruit, 198g/7oz	95

BARBECUE SAUCE

Chinese, per 15ml/1 level tablespoon	13

BARLEY, PEARL

Raw, per 28g/1oz	102
Boiled, per 28g/1oz	34
Per 15ml/1 level tablespoon, raw	45

BASS

Fillet, raw, per 28g/1oz	37
Fillet, steamed, per 28g/1oz	35

BEAN SPROUTS

Canned, per 28g/1oz	3
Raw, per 28g/1oz	8
Boiled, per 28g/1oz	7

BEAN THREADS

Dried, per 28g/1oz	110

BEANS

Per 28g/1oz

Aduki, dried	92
Aduki, boiled	40
Baked, canned in tomato sauce	18
Black, dried	96
Black, boiled or canned in brine	45
Black eye, dried	93
Black eye, boiled	38
Broad, raw	34
Broad, boiled	30
Borlotti, canned	47
Butter, dried	77
Butter, boiled	27
Cannellini, canned	25
Flageolet, dried	98
Flageolet, boiled	32
French, frozen	10
Haricot, dried	77
Haricot, boiled	26
Lima or Mung, dried	92
Mung, boiled	33
Pinto, dried	99
Pinto, boiled	41
Red Kidney, dried	77
Red Kidney, canned	25
Runner, raw	7
Runner, boiled	5
Snap, raw, green	10
Soya, dried	108
Soya, boiled	50

BEEF

Per 28g/1oz unless otherwise stated

Braising steak, standard, sold raw	50
Braising steak, lean, cubed, raw	35
Brisket, raw, lean and fat	70
Brisket, boiled, lean and fat	90
Fillet steak, medium grilled, 170g/6oz raw	250
Flash or quick fry lean beef, raw	35
Flash or quick fry lean beef, fried	45
Lean beef for stewing, raw	40
Lean boneless rib, roast, lean and fat	60
Minced beef, extra lean, raw	55
Minced beef, extra lean, fried and drained of fat	65

Minced beef, extra lean, fried and drained of fat, 28g/1oz raw weight	45
Minced beef, raw	65
Minced beef, fried, drained of fat	80
Minced beef, fried, drained of fat, 28g/1oz raw weight	50
Mini rib roast, lean and fat	90
Rump steak, raw, lean and fat	55
Rump steak, fried, lean only	55
Rump steak, grilled, lean and fat	65
Rump steak, medium grilled, 170g/6oz raw	320
Silverside, roast, lean and fat	80
Silverside, extra lean, roast, lean and fat	70
Silverside, extra lean, roast, lean only	55
Sirloin steak, medium grilled, 170g/6oz raw weight	340
Sirloin, roast, lean and fat	80
Sirloin, roast, lean only	55
Stewing steak, raw, lean and fat	50
Topside, no added fat, raw	40
Topside, no added fat, roast	50

BEEFBURGER

Average 57g/2oz beefburger, grilled	115
Average 113g/4oz beefburger, grilled	240
Average 57g/2oz low-fat beefburger, grilled	85

BEETROOT
Per 28g/1oz

Raw	8
Boiled	12
Pickled	10

BILBERRIES

Raw or frozen, per 28g/1oz	16

BISCUITS

Chocolate Digestive, per 28g/1oz	140
Digestive, plain, per 28g/1oz	134
Digestive, plain, crushed, per 15ml/1 level tablespoon	35
Gingernut, per 28g/1oz	129
Rich Tea, per 28g/1oz	126

BLACK BEAN SAUCE

Per 15ml/1 level tablespoon	25

BLACKBERRIES

Raw or frozen, per 28g/1oz	8
Stewed, without sugar, per 28g/1oz	7

BLACKCURRANTS

Raw or frozen, per 28g/1oz	8
Stewed, without sugar, per 28g/1oz	7
Canned in syrup, per 28g/1oz	23

BLACK PUDDING

Raw, per 28g/1oz	78
Sliced and fried, per 28g/1oz raw weight	85

BLOATERS

Fillet, grilled, per 28g/1oz	71
On the bone, grilled, per 28g/1oz	53

BLUEBERRIES

Raw or frozen, per 28g/1oz	18

BOMBAY MIX

Average mix, per 28g/1oz	140

BRAINS

Calves' and lambs', raw, per 28g/1oz	31
Calves', boiled, per 28g/1oz	43
Lambs', boiled, per 28g/1oz	36

BRAN

Oat Bran, per 28g/1oz	100
Soya Bran, per 28g/1oz	28
Wheat, per 28g/1oz	58

BRANDY BUTTER

Per 28g/1oz	170

BRAWN

Per 28g/1oz	43

BRAZIL NUTS

Shelled, per 28g/1oz	175
Per nut	20
Per buttered Brazil	40
Per chocolate Brazil	55

BREAD
Per 28g/1oz

Black Rye	90
Bran	65
Brown or Wheatmeal	63
Enriched, eg Cholla	110
Fried bread, 28g/1oz unfried weight	160
French	85
French, brown	75
French, wholemeal	70
Fruit bread, white	70
Fruit sesame wholemeal	120
Granary	70
Light Rye	70
Malt	70
Milk	80
Pumpernickel	60
Soda, White	75
Soft Grain White	64
Vogel	65
Wheatgerm, eg Hovis and VitBe	65
White	66
Wholemeal (100%)	61

Rolls, buns, etc, each

Baby bridge roll, 14g/½oz	35
Bagel, 42g/1½oz	150
Bap, white, 42g/1½oz	130
Bath bun, 42g/1½oz	120
Brioche roll, 50g/1¾oz	215
Chelsea bun, 92g/3¼oz	255
Croissant, 42g/1½oz	165
Croissant, 70g/2½oz	280
Crumpet, 42g/1½oz	75
Crusty roll, brown or white, 50g/1¾oz	145
Currant bun, 50g/1¾oz	150
Devonshire split, 70g/2½oz	195
Dinner roll, 42g/1½oz	130
French toast, average slice	50
Granary bap, large, 71g/2½oz	200
Hot cross bun, 57g/2oz	180
Iced Finger Bun, 64g/2¼oz	215
Jam doughnut, 78g/2¾oz	195
Morning roll, Aberdeen	185
Muffin, 64g/2¼oz	125
Pitta, white, 70g/2½oz	180
Pitta, wholemeal, 70g/2½oz	165
Scone, white, plain, 57g/2oz	160
Scone, white, fruit, 85g/3oz	210
Scone, wholemeal, fruit, 57g/2oz	150
Scotch pancake	80
Soft brown roll, 50g/1¾oz	140

Soft white roll, 50g/1¾oz	150
Staffordshire oatcake, thin, 50g/1¾oz	95
Staffordshire oatcake, thick, 85g/3oz	145
Tea cake, 57g/2oz	155
Wholemeal bap, 42g/1½oz	125
Wholemeal roll, 50g/1¾oz	125

Per 15ml/1 level tablespoon

Breadcrumbs, dried	30
Breadcrumbs, fresh	8
Bread sauce	15

BREADFRUIT

Raw, per 28g/1oz	30

BROCCOLI

Raw, per 28g/1oz	7
Boiled, per 28g/1oz	5

BRUSSELS SPROUTS

Raw, per 28g/1oz	7
Boiled, per 28g/1oz	5

BUCKLING

Fillets, per 28g/1oz	60

BUCKWHEAT

Whole grain, per 28g/1oz	100

BULGHAR WHEAT

Per 28g/1oz, raw	105

BUTTER

All brands, per 28g/1oz	210
Per 5ml/1 level teaspoon	35

C

CABBAGE, ALL TYPES

Raw, per 28g/1oz	6
Boiled, per 28g/1oz	4
Pickled red, per 15ml/1 level tablespoon	3

CANDY FLOSS

Per 28g/1oz	80
Per medium stick	60

CAPERS

Per 28g/1oz	5

CAROB POWDER

Per 28g/1oz	55

CARROTS

Raw, per 28g/1oz	6
Boiled, per 28g/1oz	5
Canned, per 28g/1oz	5
Per average carrot, 57g/2oz	12

CASHEW NUTS

Shelled, per 28g/1oz	160
Shelled, per nut	15

CASSAVA

Fresh, per 28g/1oz	43

CAULIFLOWER

Raw, per 28g/1oz	4
Boiled, per 28g/1oz	3

CAVIARE

Real, per 28g/1oz	75
Red lumpfish caviare, per 28g/1oz	27

CELERIAC

Raw, per 28g/1oz	8
Boiled, per 28g/1oz	4

CELERY

Raw, per 28g/1oz	2
Boiled, per 28g/1oz	1
Per stick of celery	5

CHEESE

Per 28g/1oz unless otherwise stated

Appenzell	113
Austrian Smoked	78
Babybel	97
Bavarian Brie with Mixed Peppers	102
Bavarian Brie with Mushrooms	110
Bavarian Smoked	80
Beaufort	129
Beaumont	113
Bel Paese	96
Bleu de Gex	116
Bleu d'Auvergne	97
Bleu des Causses	107
Bleu de Velloy	113
Blue Brie	124
Blue Cheshire	124
Blue Wensleydale	127
Bonbel	80
Bouche de Chevre	88
Boulette d'Avesnes	103
Boursin	116
Bresse Bleu	80
Brie, Danish	95
Brie, French	88
Brie, pasteurized 45% fat	107
Brie, unpasteurized 45% fat	90
Brie, 62%, Supreme	130
Caboc	155
Caerphilly	106
Caithness Full Fat Soft	110
Caithness Morven	110
Cambozola	122
Camembert, French	84
Cantal	139
Chablis-Le Soignon	113
Champs Martin Processed Walnut	107
Chaumes	105
Cheddar	117
Cheddar Farmhouse, 12 months old	146
Cheese Spread	78
Cheshire	107
Cheviot	116
Chevret	85
Cotswold	111
Cottage Cheese	27
Cow Pyrenees	102
Cream Cheese	125
Creme Polder	125
Crottin 45% fat	84
Curd Cheese	54
Danbo	97
Danish Blue Creme	107
Danish Blue	98
Danish Elbo	97
Danish Esrom	94
Danish Fynbo	101
Danish Havarti	123
Danish Maribo	103
Danish Mellow Blue	112

Danish Mycella	102
Danish Saga	129
Danish Samsoe	103
Danish Svenbo	107
Danish Tybo	91
Derby	113
Dolcellata	100
Double Gloucester	115
Doux de Montagne	90
Dutch cheese, 12% fat	62
Edam	90
Emmental	108
Etorki	134
Fetta Danish Cows	73
Fetta Greek Ewes	85
Fontina	109
Full fat soft cheese eg. Philadelphia	89
Gaperon	85
German Smoked Processed	97
Gjetost	134
Goats Milk Soft Cheese	56
Gorgonzola	112
Gouda	106
Graindorge Livarot	92
Gruyere	116
Halali Limburger	73
Halumi	84
Jarlsberg	95
La Curieuse Pont l'Eveque	94
Lancashire	106
Langres	111
Le Soignon Chevre Log	84
Le Soignon Crottin	99
Leicester	114
Leiden	101
Lymeswold, Blue or White	120
Maasdam	133
Manchego	137
Mariolles	106
Mascapone	112
Melbury	91
Momolette	89
Morbier	105
Mozzarella, Danish	92
Mozzarella, Italian	87
Munster	92
Niolo	112
Norwegian Blue	100
Olivet	96
Orangerulle	92
Orkney	115
Orkney Claymore	111
Parmesan	128
Picodon	72
Port Salut	94
Primat des Gaulles	135
Processed	94
Pyramide	98
Quark skimmed milk cheese	20
Quark low-fat cheese	35
Quark medium-fat cheese	45
Rambol with Walnuts	117
Red Windsor	114
Reduced-Fat Cheddar-Type	80

Reduced-Fat Cheshire-Type	76
Ricotta	41
Rigotte	98
Rollot	121
Roquefort	106
Royalp	110
Sage Derby	114
Saint Albray	96
Saint Nectaire	99
Sardo Pecorino	127
Shropshire Blue	116
Sprinz	124
Soya Cheese	90
St Paulin	98
Skimmed milk soft cheese	25
Stilton, Blue	117
Stilton, White	103
Taleggio	101
Tilsiter	117
Tomme Blanche	112
Tomme Grasse Tourre	105
Torta	109
Vacherin Mont d'Or	95
Wensleydale	107
Yarg	108

Per 15ml/1 level tablespoon

Cheese spread	50
Cottage cheese	15
Cream cheese	60
Curd cheese	25
Parmesan cheese, grated	30

CHERRIES

Canned in syrup, per 28g/1oz	20
Fresh, with stones, per 28g/1oz	12
Glacé, per 28g/1oz	60
Per glacé cherry or cocktail cherry	10

CHESTNUTS

Chestnut purée, sweetened, per 28g/1oz	65
Dried chestnuts, per 28g/1oz	115
Shelled, per 28g/1oz	48
With shells, per 28g/1oz	40

CHICK PEAS

Boiled, per 28g/1oz	40
Raw, per 28g/1oz	91

CHICKEN

Per 28g/1oz unless otherwise stated

Meat only, raw	34
Meat only, boiled	52
Meat only, roast	42
Meat and skin, roast	61
Chicken breast, grilled, 170g/6oz raw weight with bone	200
Chicken breast, grilled and skin removed, 170g/6oz raw weight with bone	145
Chicken drumstick, raw, 99g/3½oz	90
Chicken drumstick, grilled and skin removed, 99g/3½oz raw weight	65
Chicken drumstick, grilled, 99g/3½oz raw weight	85
Chicken leg joint, 283g/10oz raw weight	490
Chicken leg joint, skin removed 283g/10oz raw weight	205
Chicken leg joint, grilled, 283g/10oz raw weight	315
Chicken leg joint, grilled and skin removed, 283g/10oz raw weight	205

Chicken leg joint, roasted, 283g/10oz raw weight	**365**
Chicken leg joint, roasted and skin removed, 283g/10oz raw weight	**240**
Chicken leg joint, poached in stock, skin removed, 283g/10oz raw weight	**205**
Chicken thigh with skin, raw weight 120g/4¼oz	**215**
Chicken thigh, raw weight 120g/4¼oz, roasted with skin	**155**
Chicken thigh, raw weight 120g/4¼oz, roasted, skin removed	**90**
Chicken thigh, with skin, roasted, per 28g/1oz	**140**
Chicken thigh, raw weight 120g/4¼oz, grilled with skin	**150**
Chicken thigh, raw weight 120g/4¼oz, grilled, skin removed	**105**
Chicken wing quarter, average raw weight 283g/10oz, roasted with skin	**365**
Chicken wing quarter, average raw weight 283g/10oz, roasted, skin removed	**190**

CHICORY

Raw, per 28g/1oz	**3**

CHILLIES

Dried, per 28g/1oz	**85**
Fresh, flesh only, per 28g/1oz	**6**
1 medium chilli	**2**
Chilli Sauce, per 15ml/1 level tablespoon	**3**

CHINESE LEAVES

Raw, per 28g/1oz	**7**
Boiled, per 28g/1oz	**6**

CHIVES

Per 28g/1oz	**10**

CHOCOLATE

Milk or Plain, per 28g/1oz	**150**
Cooking, per 28g/1oz	**155**
Vermicelli, per 28g/1oz	**135**
Vermicelli, per 5ml/1 level teaspoon	**20**

CHOW CHOW

Sour, per 28g/1oz	**8**
Sweet, per 28g/1oz	**33**

CLAMS

Canned, per 28g/1oz	**30**
With shells, raw, per 28g/1oz	**15**
Without shells, raw, per 28g/1oz	**25**

CLEMENTINES

Average fruit with skin, 80g	**25**
Flesh only, per 28g/1oz	**13**
Flesh and skin, per 28g/1oz	**9**

COCKLES

Without shells, boiled, per 28g/1oz	**14**

COCOA POWDER

Per 28g/1oz	**88**
Per 5ml/1 level teaspoon	**10**

COCONUT

Fresh, per 28g/1oz	**100**
Desiccated, per 28g/1oz	**171**
Desiccated, per 15ml/1 level tablespoon	**30**
Fresh coconut milk, per 28ml/1floz	**6**
Coconut cream, per 28g/1oz	**95**
Creamed coconut, per 28g/1oz	**218**

COD

Per 28g/1oz unless otherwise stated

Dried, salted, boiled	**39**
Fillet, raw	**22**
Fillet, in batter, fried	**56**
Fillet in batter, deep fried, 170g/6oz raw unbattered weight	**460**
Fillet, poached in water or steamed	**24**
Frozen steaks, raw	**19**
On the bone, raw	**15**
Smoked Fillet, raw	**22**

COD LIVER OIL

Per 5ml/1 teaspoon	**40**

COD ROE

Hard roe, raw, per 28g/1oz	**32**
Hard roe, fried in egg and breadcrumbs, per 28g/1oz	**55**
Soft cod's roe, canned	**20**
Smoked roe	**50**

COFFEE

Per 28g/1oz

Coffee beans, roasted and ground, infusion	**0**
Instant	**28**
Coffee and chicory essence, per 5ml/1 teaspoon	**10**
Instant coffee, per 10ml/1 rounded teaspoon	**0**

COLEY

Fillet, raw, per 28g/1oz	**21**
On bone, steamed, per 28g/1oz	**24**
Fillet, steamed, per 28g/1oz	**28**

CORN ON THE COB

Average whole cob, 213g/7½oz	**125**

CONGER EEL

Flesh only, steamed, per 28g/1oz	**31**

CORNED BEEF

Per 28g/1oz	**62**
Corned beef in jelly, per 28g/1oz	**60**

CORNFLOUR

Per 28g/1oz	**100**
Per 15ml/1 level tablespoon	**33**

COUGH SYRUP

Thick, per 5ml/1 teaspoon	**15**
Thin, per 5ml/1 teaspoon	**5**

COURGETTES

Raw, per 28g/1oz	**4**
Sliced, fried, 28g/1oz raw weight	**15**

COUSCOUS

Raw, per 28g/1oz	**105**

CRAB

Meat only, per 28g/1oz boiled	**36**
Average crab with shell, 907g/2lb	**290**

CRANBERRIES

Raw, per 28g/1oz	**4**
Cranberry Sauce, per 28g/1oz	**65**
Cranberry Sauce, per 15ml/1 level tablespoon	**45**
Cranberry Jelly, per 28g/1oz	**40**
Cranberry Jelly, per 15ml/1 level tablespoon	**25**

CREAM

Per 28g/1oz

Aerosol Spray Cream	**95**
Clotted	**166**
Double	**125**
Extra Thick Double	**130**
Half Cream	**42**
Imitation	**85**
Non-dairy	**80**
Single	**56**
Soured	**58**
Sterilized, canned	**68**
Whipping	**105**

Per 15ml/1 level tablespoon

Aerosol Spray Cream	**7**
Clotted	**70**
Double	**55**
Extra Thick Double	**55**
Half	**20**
Imitation	**55**
Single or Soured	**25**
Sterilized, canned	**30**
Whipping	**45**

CRYSTALLIZED FRUIT

Per 28g/1oz	**75**

CUCUMBER

Raw, per 28g/1oz	**3**

CURRANTS, DRIED

Per 28g/1oz	**69**
Per 15ml/1 level tablespoon	**20**

CURRY PASTE

Per 28g/1oz	**40**
Per 5ml/1 level teaspoon	**7**

CURRY POWDER

Per 28g/1oz	**66**
Per 5ml/1 level teaspoon	**12**

CUSTARD

Per 142ml/¼ pint, made as instructed

With semi-skimmed milk	**135**
With Silver Top milk	**155**
With skimmed milk	**110**

CUSTARD APPLE

Flesh only, raw, per 28g/1oz	**25**

CUSTARD POWDER

Per 28g/1oz	**100**
Per 15ml/1 level tablespoon	**33**

D

DAMSONS

Fresh, with stones, per 28g/1oz	**11**
Stewed, with stones, no sugar, per 28g/1oz	**8**

DASHEEN

Per 28g/1oz	**32**

DATES

Per 28g/1oz

Dried, with stones	**60**
Dried, without stones	**70**
Fresh with stones	**30**
Chopped and sugar rolled	**77**
Per fresh date	**15**
Per dried date	**15**

DOVER SOLE

Fillet, raw, per 28g/1oz	**23**
Fillet, fried in breadcrumbs, per 28g/1oz	**61**
Fillet, steamed or poached, per 28g/1oz	**26**
On the bone, steamed or poached, per 28g/1oz	**18**

DRIPPING

Per 28g/1oz	**253**
Per 15ml/1 level tablespoon	**125**

DUCK

Per 28g/1oz unless otherwise stated

Raw, meat only	35
Raw, meat, fat and skin	122
Roast, meat only	54
Roast, meat, fat and skin	96
Leg and thigh joint, roasted, 312g/11oz raw weight	410
Leg and thigh joint, roasted and skin and fat removed, 312g/11oz raw weight	155
Breast and wing joint, roasted, 397g/14oz raw weight	440
Breast and wing joint, roasted and skin and fat removed, 397g/14oz raw weight	135

E

EEL

Meat only, raw, per 28g/1oz	48
Meat only, stewed, per 28g/1oz	57
Jellied eels plus some jelly, per 28g/1oz	60
Smoked, per 28g/1oz	55

EGGS, each, raw

Size 1	95
Size 2	90
Size 3	80
Size 4	75
Size 5	70
Size 6	60
Yolk of size 3 egg	65
White of size 3 egg	15

Each, fried

Size 1	115
Size 2	110
Size 3	100
Size 4	95
Size 5	90
Size 6	80
Duck, medium, 100g/3½oz	170
Goose, per 28g/1oz	52
Quails, each	15
Turkey, per 28g/1oz	48

ENDIVE

Raw, per 28g/1oz	3

F

FENNEL, FLORENCE

Raw, per 28g/1oz	6
Boiled, per 28g/1oz	8

FIGS

Canned in syrup, per 28g/1oz	19
Dried, per 28g/1oz	60
Fresh, green, per 28g/1oz	12
Fresh, each, 30g	15
Per dried fig	30

FIVE SPICE POWDER

Per 28g/1oz	0

FLOUR

Per 28g/1oz

Buckwheat	99
Granary	99
Maizemeal or Cornmeal (96%)	103
Maizemeal or Cornmeal (60%)	100
Potato or Rice	100
Rye (100%)	95
Soya, low-fat	100
Soya, full-fat	127
Wheatmeal	93
White, plain	99
White, self-raising	96
White, strong	96
Wholemeal, plain	90
Wholemeal, self-raising	80
Yam	90

Per 15ml/1 level tablespoon

White or Wholemeal	30

FLOUNDER

On the bone, raw, per 28g/1oz	20
On the bone, steamed, per 28g/1oz	15

FRENCH DRESSING

Per 15ml/1 tablespoon	75
Oil-free, per 15ml/1 tablespoon	3

FROGS' LEGS

Raw, meat only, per 28g/1oz	20

FROMAGE FRAIS

Per 28g/1oz

Fromage Frais, natural	32
Fromage Frais, 0% Fat	15

Per 15ml/1 level tablespoon

Fromage Frais, natural	15
Fromage Frais, 0%	7

FRUCTOSE

Per 28g/1oz	105
Per 15ml/1 level tablespoon	40

G

GAMMON

Per 28g/1oz unless otherwise stated

Gammon joint, raw, lean and fat	67
Gammon joint, boiled, lean and fat	76
Gammon joint, boiled, lean only	47
Gammon, raw, lean only	23
Gammon rashers, grilled, lean and fat	65
Gammon rashers, grilled, lean only	49
Gammon rasher, well grilled, 170g/6oz raw	260
Gammon, roast, lean only	60

GARLIC

One clove	0

GELATINE

Per 28g/1oz	96
Per 15ml/1 level tablespoon	30
Per envelope, 10g	35

GHEE

Per 28g/1oz	255
Per 15ml/1 level tablespoon	135

GHERKINS

Per 28g/1oz	5

GINGER

Ground, per 28g/1oz	73
Ground, per 5ml/1 level teaspoon	8
Root, raw, peeled, per 28g/1oz	18
Stem, in syrup, drained, per 28g/1oz	60
Stem in syrup, drained, per medium piece	40
Syrup from stem ginger, per 28g/1oz	55

GOLDEN SYRUP

Per 28g/1oz	84
Per 15ml/1 level tablespoon	60

GOOSE

Roast, meat only (without skin), per 28g/1oz	90

GOOSEBERRIES

Fresh, ripe dessert, per 28g/1oz	10
Fresh, cooking, per 28g/1oz	5
Canned in syrup, per 28g/1oz	22

GRAPEFRUIT

Canned in natural juice, per 28g/1oz	11
Canned in syrup, per 28g/1oz	17
Flesh only, per 28g/1oz	6
Flesh and skin, per 28g/1oz	3
Medium whole fruit, 454g/1lb	50
Juice, sweetened, per 28ml/1floz	11
Juice, unsweetened, per 28ml/1floz	9

GRAPEFRUIT, PINK

Flesh with skin, per 28g/1oz	2
Flesh only, per 28g/1oz	8
Juice, per 28ml/1floz	10
Medium whole fruit, 454g/1lb	80

GRAPES

Black, per 28g/1oz	14
White, per 28g/1oz	17
Grape juice, per 28ml/1floz	14

GRAVY

Thick, made with meat dripping, 30ml/2 tablespoons	30
Thick, made without fat, per 30ml/2 tablespoons	10
Thin, made without fat, per 30ml/2 tablespoons	5

GREENGAGES

Fresh, with stones, per 28g/1oz	13
Stewed, with stones, no sugar, per 28g/1oz	11

GRENADINE SYRUP

Per 28g/1oz	72

GROUSE

Roast, meat only, per 28g/1oz	49
Roast, on the bone, per 28g/1oz	32

GUAVAS

Fresh, with seeds, per 28g/1oz	16
Canned in syrup, per 28g/1oz	17
Canned in natural juice, per 28g/1oz	12

GUINEA FOWL

Roast, on the bone, per 28g/1oz	32
Roast, meat only, per 28g/1oz	60

H

HADDOCK

Per 28g/1oz unless otherwise stated

Fillet, raw	21
Fillet in breadcrumbs, fried	49

On the bone, raw	15
On the bone, in breadcrumbs, fried	45
Smoked, raw	25
Smoked fillet, steamed or poached in water	29
Finnan haddock fillet	21

HAGGIS

Cooked, per 28g/1oz	88

HAKE
Per 28g/1oz

Fillet, raw	20
Fillet, steamed	30
Fillet, fried in breadcrumbs	58
On the bone, raw	10

HALIBUT

Fillet, raw, per 28g/1oz	30
Fillet, steamed, per 28g/1oz	37
On the bone, raw, per 28g/1oz	26
On the bone, steamed, per 28g/1oz	28

HALVA

Per 28g/1oz	125

HAM
Per 28g/1oz unless otherwise stated

Chopped ham roll or loaf	70
Ham, boiled, lean	47
Ham, vacuum-packed, lean only	30
Parma ham, lean and fat	85
Parma ham, lean only	60
Ham steak, well grilled, 99g/3½oz raw weight	105
Shoulder, vacuum-packed, lean only	35

HARE

Stewed, meat only, per 28g/1oz	54
Stewed, on the bone, per 28g/1oz	39

HAZELNUTS

Shelled, per 28g/1oz	180
Per nut	8
Chocolate hazelnut whirls, each	40

HEART

Lamb's, raw, per 28g/1oz	34
Ox, raw, per 28g/1oz	31
Pig's, raw, per 28g/1oz	26

HERRING
Per 28g/1oz unless otherwise stated

Fillet, raw	66
Fillet, grilled	56
Fillet in oatmeal, fried	66
On the bone, grilled	38
On the bone in oatmeal, fried	58
Rollmop herring	47
Rollmop herring, 71g/2½oz weight	120
Whole herring, grilled, 128g/4½oz raw weight	170

HERRING ROE

Soft, fried, per 28g/1oz	69
Soft, raw, per 28g/1oz	23
Per 106g/3¾oz can	135

HONEY

Per 28g/1oz	82
Per 5ml/1 level teaspoon	20

HORSERADISH

Fresh root, per 28g/1oz	17
Sauce, per 15ml/1 level tablespoon	13
Creamed, per 15ml/1 level tablespoon	35

HUMUS

Per 28g/1oz	50

HUNDREDS AND THOUSANDS

Per 5ml/1 level teaspoon	15

HUSS

Raw, flesh only, per 28g/1oz	35

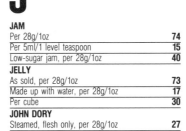

ICE CREAM

Soft ice cream (eg Mr Whippy), per 28g/1oz	45
Vanilla, dairy, per 28g/1oz	55
Vanilla, non-dairy, per 28g/1oz	50

ICE CREAM CONES

Large	15
Medium	10
Sugar	40
Wafers	5

ICING

Fondant, per 28g/1oz	110
Royal, per 28g/1oz	85

JAM

Per 28g/1oz	74
Per 5ml/1 level teaspoon	15
Low-sugar jam, per 28g/1oz	40

JELLY

As sold, per 28g/1oz	73
Made up with water, per 28g/1oz	17
Per cube	30

JOHN DORY

Steamed, flesh only, per 28g/1oz	27

K

KALE

Leaves without stems, raw, per 28g/1oz	15
Leaves without stems, cooked, per 28g/1oz	11

KIDNEY

All types, raw, per 28g/1oz	25
Lamb's kidney, fried, 57g/2oz raw weight	65

KIPPERS

Fillet, raw, per 28g/1oz	75
Fillet, baked or grilled, per 28g/1oz	58
On the bone, baked, per 28g/1oz	31
Whole kipper, grilled, 170g/6oz raw weight	280

KIWI FRUIT

Per 28g/1oz	16
Average whole kiwi fruit	35

KUMQUAT

Per 28g/1oz	18
Each	5

L

LAMB
Per 28g/1oz unless otherwise stated

Best end neck lamb cutlets, on the bone, grilled, lean and fat	85
Best end neck lamb cutlets, on the bone, grilled, 75g/2¾oz raw weight	165
Braising steak, lean, trimmed and cubed, raw	40
Braising steak, lean, trimmed and cubed, grilled on kebabs, 28g/1oz raw weight	35
Breast, boned, raw, lean and fat	100
Breast, boned, roast, lean and fat	110
Chump steaks, boneless, raw, lean and fat	65
Chump steak, boneless, raw, lean & fat, 130g/4½oz	285
Chump steak, boneless, grilled, lean and fat, 130g/4½oz raw weight	220
Leg, raw, lean and fat	90
Leg, raw, lean only	35
Leg, roast, lean and fat	85
Leg, roast, lean only	55
Leg steak, grilled, 198g/7oz raw weight	270
Loin chop, raw, lean and fat, without bone	105
Loin chop, raw, lean and fat, 120g/4¼oz	385
Loin chop, grilled, lean and fat, 120g/4¼oz raw weight	265
Loin chop, extra trimmed, raw, lean and fat, off bone	80
Loin chop, extra trimmed, raw, lean and fat, on the bone, 105g/3¾oz	225
Loin chop, extra trimmed, grilled, lean and fat, on the bone, 105g/3¾oz raw weight	190
Minced lamb, lean, raw	60
Minced lamb, fried and drained of fat	75
Minced lamb, fried, drained of fat, 28g/1oz raw weight	45
Neck fillets, raw, lean and fat	65
Shoulder, raw, lean and fat	75
Shoulder, raw, lean only	35
Shoulder, roast, lean and fat	85
Shoulder, roast, lean only	60

LARD

Per 28g/1oz	253
Per 15ml/1 level tablespoon	125

LAVERBREAD

Per 28g/1oz	15

LEEKS

Raw, per 28g/1oz	9
Boiled	7
Average whole leek, raw	25

LEMON

Flesh and skin, per 28g/1oz	4
Lemon juice, per 15ml/1 tablespoon	0

LEMON CURD

Per 28g/1oz	80
Per 5ml/1 level teaspoon	15

LEMON SOLE

Lemon sole fillet, per 28g/1oz	23
Fillet, steamed or poached, per 28g/1oz	26
On the bone, steamed or poached, per 28g/1oz	18

LENTILS

Brown, raw, per 28g/1oz	104
Brown, boiled, per 28g/1oz	32
Green, raw, per 28g/1oz	93
Green, boiled, per 28g/1oz	35
Red, raw, per 28g/1oz	86
Red, boiled, per 28g/1oz	28

LETTUCE

Fresh, per 28g/1oz	3

LIME PICKLE

Per 28g/1oz	72

LIQUID GLUCOSE

Per 28ml/1floz	90

LIVER

Per 28g/1oz unless otherwise stated

Calves', raw	43
Calves', fried	72
Chickens', raw	38
Chickens', fried	55
Lambs', raw	51
Lambs', fried	66
Ox, raw	46
Pigs', raw	44
Turkeys', raw	37

LIVER SAUSAGE

Per 28g/1oz	68

LOBSTER

With shell, boiled, per 28g/1oz	12
Meat only, boiled, per 28g/1oz	34

LOGANBERRIES

Fresh, per 28g/1oz	5
Canned in syrup, per 28g/1oz	29
Canned in natural juice, per 28g/1oz	15

LOTUS TUBES

Canned, per 28g/1oz	4

LOW-FAT SPREAD

Per 28g/1oz	110
Per 5ml/1 level teaspoon	15
Very Low Fat Spread, per 28g/1oz	77

LUNCHEON MEAT

Per 28g/1oz	89

LYCHEES

Fresh, flesh only, per 28g/1oz	18
Canned, per 28g/1oz	19
Per lychee	8

M

MACEDONIA NUTS

Shelled, per 28g/1oz	188

MACKEREL

Per 28g/1oz unless otherwise stated

Fillet, raw	63
Fillet, fried	53
Fillet, grilled	42
On the bone, fried	39
On the bone, grilled	37
Kippered mackerel	62
Smoked mackerel	70
Whole raw mackerel, 227g/8oz	320
Whole mackerel, grilled, 320g/12oz raw weight	245

MAIZE

Wholegrain, per 28g/1oz	103

MALT EXTRACT

Per 28g/1oz	85
Per 15ml/1 level tablespoon	60

MANDARINS

Canned in natural juice, per 28g/1oz	11
Canned, in syrup, per 28g/1oz	16
Fresh, with skin, per 28g/1oz	7
Whole fruit, 85g/3oz	20

MANGETOUT

Raw, per 28g/1oz	16
Boiled, per 28g/1oz	12

MANGO

Raw, flesh only, per 28g/1oz	17
Dried, per 28g/1oz	80
Canned, fruit and syrup, per 28g/1oz	22
Medium whole mango, 283g/10oz	100
Mango chutney, per 15ml/1 level tablespoon	40

MANGOSTEEN

Average whole fruit, 65g	20

MAPLE SYRUP

Per 28g/1oz	70
Per 15ml/1 level tablespoon	50

MARGARINE

All brands, including those labelled 'high in polyunsaturates', per 28g/1oz	210
Per 5ml/1 level teaspoon	35

MARMALADE

Per 28g/1oz	74
Per 5ml/1 level teaspoon	15
Low-sugar marmalade, per 28g/1oz	40

MARRON GLACÉ

Per 28g/1oz	74
One medium marron glacé	45

MARROW

Raw, per 28g/1oz	5
Boiled, per 28g/1oz	2

MARZIPAN (ALMOND PASTE)

Per 28g/1oz	126

MAYONNAISE

Per 28g/1oz	205
Per 15ml/1 level tablespoon	120

MEDLARS

Flesh only, per 28g/1oz	12

MEGRIM

Fillet, raw, per 28g/1oz	22
Fillet, steamed, per 28g/1oz	27

MELON

Per 28g/1oz unless otherwise stated

Cantaloupe, flesh only	7
Cantaloupe, with skin	4
Charentais, flesh only	5
Galia, flesh only	8
Galia, with skin	6
Honeydew or Yellow, flesh only	6
Honeydew or Yellow, with skin	4
Ogen, with skin	5
Watermelon, flesh only	6
Watermelon, with skin	3
Melon seeds, coat removed	165
Slice of Cantaloupe, Honeydew or Yellow with skin, 227g/8oz	30

MERINGUE

Shells, unfilled, per 28g/1oz	108
Nest, average	65

MILK

Per 568ml/1 pint unless otherwise stated

Buttermilk	210
Channel Island or Gold Top	445
Evaporated milk, full cream, reconstituted	360
Goat's	340
Instant spray dried low-fat skimmed milk, reconstituted	200
Instant dried skimmed milk with vegetable fat, reconstituted	280
Instant low-fat milk, dry, per 28g/1oz	100
Longlife or UHT Whole Milk	380
Pasteurized Silver Top	380
Pasteurized Silver Top, cream removed, 510ml/18floz	240
Semi-skimmed milk	260
Skimmed milk	190
Soya milk, diluted as directed	370
Sterilized whole milk	380
Untreated farm milk or Green Top	380

Per 15ml/1 tablespoon

Channel Island or Gold Top	15
Condensed, full cream, sweetened	50
Condensed, skimmed, sweetened	40
Evaporated full cream	23
Instant low-fat milk, dry	18
Instant low-fat milk, reconstituted	5
Skimmed	5
Whole milk	10

Canned milk, per 28ml/1floz

Evaporated full-fat milk	43
Condensed, skimmed, sweetened	76
Condensed, full-fat, sweetened	94

MILLET

Per 28g/1oz	100

MINCEMEAT

Per 28g/1oz	67
Per 15ml/1 level tablespoon	40

MINCE PIE

Medium pie, 57g/2oz	250

MINT

Fresh, per 28g/1oz	3

MINT SAUCE

Per 15ml/1 tablespoon	5

MISO

Per 28g/1oz	51
Per 15ml/1 level tablespoon	33

MIXED PEEL, CANDIED

Per 28g/1oz	90

MOLASSES

Per 28g/1oz	78
Per 15ml/1 tablespoon	45

MONKFISH

Raw, flesh only, per 28g/1oz	20
Smoked, per 28g/1oz	31
Steamed, flesh only, per 28g/1oz	28

MOOLI

Raw, flesh only, per 28g/1oz	5

MULBERRIES

Raw, per 28g/1oz	10

MULLET

Grey fillet, raw, per 28g/1oz	40
Grey fillet, steamed, per 28g/1oz	35
Red fillet, raw, per 28g/1oz	45

MUSHROOMS

Raw, per 28g/1oz	4
Button, fried whole, 57g/2oz raw weight	80
Button, sliced and fried, 57g/2oz raw weight	100
Chinese, dried, per 28g/1oz	80
Dried, per 28g/1oz	40
Flat, fried whole, 57g/2oz raw weight	120
Flat, sliced and fried, 57g/2oz raw weight	150
Straw, canned, drained, per 28g/1oz	9

MUSSELS

With shells, boiled, per 28g/1oz	7
Without shells, boiled, per 28g/1oz	25
Per 250g can in brine or natural juice, drained	150

MUSTARD & CRESS

Raw, per 28g/1oz	3
Whole carton	5

MUSTARD

Dry, per 28g/1oz	128
Made, English, or French, per 5ml/1 level teaspoon	10

N

NECTARINES

Fresh, with stone, per 28g/1oz	13
Medium whole nectarine, 170g/6oz	80

NOODLES

Boiled, per 28g/1oz	33
Fresh, per 28g/1oz	80
Dried, per 28g/1oz	102

NUTMEG

Powdered, per 2.5ml/½level teaspoon	0

NUTS

Chopped mixed nuts, per 28g/1oz	160
Per 5ml/1 level teaspoon	10

O

OATMEAL

Raw, per 28g/1oz	114
Raw, per 15ml/1 level tablespoon	40

OATS

Rolled, per 28g/1oz	115

OCTOPUS

Raw, per 28g/1oz	20

OIL

Corn, olive, sunflower seed, vegetable or solid vegetable oil etc, per 28g/1oz	255
All varieties, per 15ml/1 level tablespoon	120

OKRA (LADIES' FINGERS)

Raw, per 28g/1oz	5

OLIVES

Stoned, in brine, per 28g/1oz	29
With stones, in brine, per 28g/1oz	23
Per black olive	3
Per stuffed olive	5

ONIONS

Raw, per 28g/1oz	7
Boiled, per 28g/1oz	4
Chopped and fried, per 28g/1oz	98
Sliced and fried, 28g/1oz raw weight	45
Onion rings in batter, fried, per 28g/1oz	145
Dried, per 15ml/1 level tablespoon	10
Whole medium onion, raw, 113g/4oz	28
Pickled onion, each	5
Cocktail onion, each	1
Spring onion, each	3

ORANGES

Per 28g/1oz unless otherwise stated

Flesh only	10
Flesh with skin	7
Juice, sweetened, per 28ml/1floz	15
Juice, unsweetened, per 28ml/1floz	11
Juice, unsweetened, per 15ml/1 tablespoon	6
Whole fruit, small, 142g/5oz	35
Whole fruit, medium, 227g/8oz	60
Whole fruit, large, 283g/10oz	75

ORTANIQUES

Flesh only, per 28g/1oz	16
Flesh with skin, per 28g/1oz	12
Whole fruit, 142g/5oz	60

OXTAIL

Stewed, without bone, per 28g/1oz	69
On the bone, stewed and skimmed of fat, per 28g/1oz	26

OYSTERS

With shells, raw, per 28g/1oz	2
Without shells, raw, per 28g/1oz	14
Per oyster	5

OYSTER SAUCE

Per 15ml/1 level tablespoon	12

P

PARSLEY

Fresh, per 28g/1oz	6

PARSNIPS

Raw, peeled, per 28g/1oz	14
Boiled, per 28g/1oz	16
Roast, per 28g/1oz	30

PARTRIDGE

Roast, on bone, per 28g/1oz	36
Roast, meat only, per 28g/1oz	60

PASSION FRUIT

Flesh only, per 28g/1oz	10
With skin, per 28g/1oz	4
Average whole fruit	6

PASTA

White, fresh, all shapes, per 28g/1oz	80
White, dry, raw, all shapes, per 28g/1oz	105
White, dry, boiled, all shapes, per 28g/1oz	33
Wholewheat, dry, raw, all shapes, per 28g/1oz	95
Wholewheat, dry, boiled, all shapes, per 28g/1oz	34

PASTRAMI

Per 28g/1oz	65

PASTRY

Choux, raw, per 28g/1oz	61
Choux, baked, per 28g/1oz	94
Flaky, raw, per 28g/1oz	121
Flaky, baked, per 28g/1oz	160
Phyllo, raw, per 28g/1oz	94
Puff, frozen, raw, per 28g/1oz	115
Shortcrust, raw, per 28g/1oz	129
Shortcrust, baked, per 28g/1oz	149
Wholemeal, raw, per 28g/1oz	125
Wholemeal, baked, per 28g/1oz	145

PAW PAW (PAPAYA)

Canned in syrup, per 28g/1oz	18
Fresh, flesh only, per 28g/1oz	11
Whole medium-sized fruit, 340g/12oz	80

PEACHES

Canned in syrup, per 28g/1oz	25
Canned, half peach, drained	25
Canned in natural juice, per 28g/1oz	13
Per half peach, canned in natural juice, drained	15
Dried, per 28g/1oz	60
Dried, per half peach	35
Fresh, with stone, per 28g/1oz	9
Whole fruit, 170g/6oz	55

PEANUTS

Shelled, fresh, per 28g/1oz	162
Dry roasted, per 28g/1oz	160
Roasted and salted, per 28g/1oz	162
Peanut butter, per 28g/1oz	177
Peanut butter, per 5ml/1 level teaspoon	35
Per peanut	5

PEARS

Cooking pears, raw, peeled, per 28g/1oz	10
Dessert pears, whole, per 28g/1oz	8
Dried, per 28g/1oz	45
Canned in syrup, per 28g/1oz	22
Canned in syrup, drained, per half pear	30
Canned in natural juice, per 28g/1oz	11
Whole fruit, 170g/6oz	50

PEAS

Per 28g/1oz

Fresh, raw	19
Frozen, raw	15
Canned, garden	13
Canned, processed	23
Dried, raw	81
Dried, boiled	29
Split, raw	88
Split, boiled	33

PECANS

Per 28g/1oz	195
Per nut	15

PEPPER

Ground, per pinch	0

PEPPERS (PIMENTOS)

Green, yellow or black, per 28g/1oz	8
Orange or Red, per 28g/1oz	10
Average green pepper, 142g/5oz	30

PERCH

White, raw, per 28g/1oz	35
Yellow, raw, per 28g/1oz	25

PHEASANT

Meat only, roast, per 28g/1oz	60

On the bone, roast, per 28g/1oz	38
PIGEON	
Meat only, roast, per 28g/1oz	65
On the bone, roast, per 28g/1oz	29
PIKE	
Fillet, raw, per 28g/1oz	25
PILCHARDS	
Canned in tomato sauce, per 28g/1oz	36
PIMENTOS	
Canned in brine, drained, per 28g/1oz	6
PINE NUTS	
Per 28g/1oz	180
PINEAPPLE	
Canned in natural juice, per 28g/1oz	15
Canned in syrup, per 28g/1oz	22
Fresh, flesh only, per 28g/1oz	13
Slice of fresh pineapple, with skin and core, 142g/5oz	35
Ring of canned, drained pineapple in syrup	35
Ring of canned, drained pineapple in natural juice	20
Pineapple juice, per 28ml/1floz	13
PISTACHIO NUTS	
Shelled, per 28g/1oz	180
Per nut	10
PLAICE	
Fillet, raw or steamed, per 28g/1oz	26
Fillet, in batter, fried, per 28g/1oz	79
Fillet, in breadcrumbs, fried, per 28g/1oz	65
PLANTAIN	
Green, raw, per 28g/1oz	32
Green, boiled, per 28g/1oz	35
Ripe, fried, per 28g/1oz	76
PLUMS	
Per 28g/1oz unless otherwise stated	
Cooking plums, with stones, raw	7
Cooking plums with stones, stewed without sugar	6
Fresh dessert plums, with stones, raw	10
POLLACK	
On the bone, raw, per 28g/1oz	25
POMEGRANATE	
Flesh only, per 28g/1oz	20
Whole pomegranate, 198g/7oz	65
POMELO	
Flesh only, per 28g/1oz	13
Flesh with skin, per 28g/1oz	6
Whole fruit, 822g/29oz	175
POPCORN	
Per 28g/1oz	110
PORK	
Per 28g/1oz unless otherwise stated	
Collar, trimmed of all visible fat, raw	50
Crackling, average portion, 9g/⅓oz	65
Fillet, raw lean only	35
Front (rib belly), trimmed of all visible fat, raw	55
Ground or minced pork, raw	65
Ground or minced pork, fried and drained of fat	90
Ground or minced pork, fried and drained of fat, 28g/1oz raw weight	65
Lean pork mince, raw	55
Lean pork mince, fried and drained of fat	80
Lean pork mince, fried and drained of fat, 28g/1oz raw weight	50
Hand (front leg), trimmed of all visible fat, raw	40

Lean cubed leg of pork, raw	35
Leg, boneless, extra trimmed, lean only, raw	30
Leg, boneless, extra trimmed, roast, lean only	35
Loin chops, boneless, extra trimmed, grilled	65
Loin chop, boneless, extra trimmed, 103g raw	165
Pork lean braising steak, cubed, raw	35
Pork lean braising steak, cubed, cooked	45
Rib loin, trimmed of all visible fat, raw	50
Rump belly, trimmed of all visible fat, raw	40
Rump loin, trimmed of all visible fat, raw	35
Shoulder, extra trimmed, raw, lean only	30
Shoulder, extra trimmed, roast, lean only	40
Tenderloin, raw, lean only	35
POTATOES	
Per 28g/1oz unless otherwise stated	
Raw, peeled	21
Baked, weighed with skin	24
Boiled, old potatoes	23
Boiled, new potatoes	22
Canned, new potatoes, drained	15
Canned, new potatoes, per 283g/10oz can	135
Chips, (average thickness)	72
Crisps	150
Roast, large chunks	40
Roast, medium chunks	45
Roast, small chunks	50
Sauté	40
Instant mashed potato powder, dry	90
Instant mashed potato powder, 1 level tablespoon, dry	40
Jacket-baked potato, 198g/7oz raw weight	150
Jacket-baked potato, 283g/10oz raw weight	210
Mashed potato, 142g/5oz raw weight mashed with 45ml/3 tablespoons Silver Top milk and 7g/¼oz knob butter	205
Roast potato, medium chunk, 50g/1¾oz	80
POTATO FLOUR	
Per 28g/1oz	100
POUSSIN	
1 medium whole poussin, roasted, 454g/1lb raw weight, meat and skin	395
1 medium whole poussin, roasted, 454g/1lb raw weight, meat only	210
PRAWNS	
With shells, per 28g/1oz	12
Without shells, per 28g/1oz	30
PRICKLY PEAR	
Pulp and small seeds, per 28g/1oz	15
PRUNES	
Per 28g/1oz unless otherwise stated	
Dried, raw, with stones	38
Dried, raw, no stones	46
Stewed, without sugar, fruit and juice with stones	21
No-need-to-soak, weighed with stones	33
Prune juice	25
Per prune	10
PUMPKIN	
Flesh only, raw, per 28g/1oz	7
Pumpkin seeds, seed coat removed, per 28g/1oz	173

Q

QUAIL	
Raw, flesh only, per 28g/1oz	37
Whole quail, raw, with skin, 113g/4oz	105
Whole quail, raw, without skin, 113g/4oz whole weight	65
QUINCES	
Flesh only, raw, per 28g/1oz	7

R

RABBIT	
Meat only, raw, per 28g/1oz	35
Meat only, stewed, per 28g/1oz	51
On the bone, stewed, per 28g/1oz	26
RADICCHIO	
Per 28g/1oz	3
RADISHES	
Fresh, per 28g/1oz	4
Per radish	2
RAISINS	
Dried, per 28g/1oz	70
Per 15ml/1 level tablespoon	25
Yogurt coated raisins, per 28g/1oz	110
RASPBERRIES	
Fresh or frozen, per 28g/1oz	7
Canned in syrup, per 28g/1oz	25
Canned in natural juice, per 28g/1oz	10
RED SNAPPER	
Fillet, raw, per 28g/1oz	26
REDCURRANTS	
Fresh, per 28g/1oz	6
Redcurrant jelly, per 5ml/1 level teaspoon	15
RHUBARB	
Raw, per 28g/1oz	2
Canned in syrup	15
Stewed without sugar, per 28g/1oz	2
RICE	
Per 28g/1oz	
Brown, raw	99
Brown, boiled	33
Chinese glutinous	102
Ground, raw	100
Vermicelli	105
White, raw	102
White, boiled	35
Wild, raw	105
Wild, boiled	49
Per 15ml/1 level tablespoon	
Boiled	20
Fried	35
Ground, raw	35
Raw	35
ROCK	
Edinburgh rock, per 28g/1oz	102
Seaside rock, per 28g/1oz	95
ROSE HIP SYRUP	
Per 28g/1oz	65

Per 15ml/1 tablespoon	**45**
Unsweetened, per 15ml/1 tablespoon	**20**

S

SAGO

Raw, per 28g/1oz	**101**

SALAMI

Belgian or Hungarian, per 28g/1oz	**130**
Danish, per 28g/1oz	**160**
German, per 28g/1oz	**120**

SALMON

Canned, per 28g/1oz	**44**
Fillet, raw, per 28g/1oz	**52**
Fillet, steamed, per 28g/1oz	**56**
On the bone, steamed, per 28g/1oz	**45**
Smoked, per 28g/1oz	**63**
Steak, raw, 198g/7oz	**235**

SALMON TROUT

Raw, flesh only, per 28g/1oz	**50**

SALSIFY

Boiled, per 28g/1oz	**5**

SALT

Per 28g/1oz	**0**

SARDINES

Raw, per 28g/1oz	**55**
Canned in oil, drained, per 28g/1oz	**62**
Canned in tomato sauce, per 28g/1oz	**50**

SATSUMAS

Flesh only, per 28g/1oz	**12**
1 medium fruit, 70g/2½oz	**20**

SAUERKRAUT

Canned, per 28g/1oz	**5**

SAUSAGES

Per sausage, grilled

Beef, small or thin	**70**
Beef, large or thick	**120**
Beef, skinless	**70**
Cocktail	**40**
Cumberland, large or thick	**180**
Pork, small or thin	**75**
Pork, large or thick	**140**
Pork, skinless	**75**
Pork, low-fat, small or thin	**60**
Pork, low-fat, large or thick	**90**
Pork & Beef, low-fat, small or thin	**50**
Pork & Beef, low-fat, large or thick	**90**
Pork & Beef, small or thin	**75**
Pork & Beef, large or thick	**130**

SAUSAGES, DELICATESSEN

Per 28g/1oz

Belgian Liver Sausage	**90**
Bierwurst	**75**
Bockwurst	**180**
Cervelat	**140**
Chorizo	**140**
Continental Liver Sausage	**85**
French Garlic Sausage	**90**
Garlic Sausage	**70**
Ham Sausage	**45**
Kabanos	**115**

Krakowska	**80**
Mettwurst	**120**
Mortadella, Italian	**105**
Polish Country Sausage	**60**
Polony	**80**
Pork Boiling Ring, Coarse	**110**
Smoked Dutch Sausage	**105**
Smoked Ham Sausage	**65**
Smoked Pork Sausage	**130**

SAUSAGEMEAT

Pork, per 28g/1oz raw	**80**

SAVELOY

Raw, per 28g/1oz	**74**

SCALLOPS

Raw, without shells, per 28g/1oz	**20**
Steamed, without shells, per 28g/1oz	**30**

SCAMPI

Fried in breadcrumbs, per 28g/1oz	**90**
Peeled, raw, per 28g/1oz	**30**

SEAKALE

Boiled, per 28g/1oz	**2**

SEMOLINA

Raw, per 28g/1oz	**99**

SESAME SEEDS

Per 28g/1oz	**168**
Per 15ml/1 level tablespoon	**55**

SHARK

Raw, flesh only, per 28g/1oz	**50**

SHARON FRUIT

Per 28g/1oz	**22**
Per medium whole sharon fruit	**130**

SHRIMPS

Canned, drained, per 28g/1oz	**27**
Dried	**69**
Fresh, with shells	**11**
Fresh, without shells	**33**

SKATE

Raw, flesh only, per 28g/1oz	**27**
Fillet, in batter, fried, weighed with bones, per 28g/1oz	**57**

SMELTS

Without heads, fried, per 28g/1oz	**116**

SNAILS

Flesh only, per 28g/1oz	**25**

SOLID VEGETABLE OIL

Per 28g/1oz	**255**

SOY SAUCE

Per 28g/1oz	**20**
Per 15ml/1 tablespoon	**13**

SOYA BRAN

Per 28g/1oz	**55**

SOYA MILK

Per 568ml/1 pint	**222**

SPINACH

Boiled, per 28g/1oz	**9**
Raw, per 28g/1oz	**7**

SPRATS

Fried without heads, per 28g/1oz	**110**
Smoked fillets, per 28g/1oz	**63**

SPRING GREENS

Boiled, per 28g/1oz	**3**

SPRING ONIONS

Raw, per 28g/1oz	**10**

SQUASH

Acorn, raw, per 28g/1oz	**12**
Butternut, raw, per 28g/1oz	**15**
Spaghetti, raw, per 28g/1oz	**7**

SQUID

Flesh only, raw, per 28g/1oz	**25**

STRAWBERRIES

Per 28g/1oz

Fresh or frozen	**7**
Canned in natural juice	**10**
Canned in syrup	**23**

SUET

Block, per 28g/1oz	**255**
Shredded, per 28g/1oz	**235**
Shredded, per 15ml/1 level tablespoon	**85**
Vegetable, per 28g/1oz	**243**

SUGAR

White, brown, Demerara, icing, caster or granulated, per 28g/1oz	**112**
Per 5ml/1 level teaspoon	**17**
Large sugar lump	**20**
Small sugar lump	**10**

SULTANAS

Dried, per 28g/1oz	**71**
Per 15ml/1 level tablespoon	**25**

SUNFLOWER SEEDS

Per 28g/1oz, coat removed	**170**

SWEDES

Raw, per 28g/1oz	**6**
Boiled, per 28g/1oz	**5**

SWEETBREADS

Lamb, raw, per 28g/1oz	**37**
Lamb, fried, per 28g/1oz	**65**

SWEETCORN

Canned in brine, per 28g/1oz	**22**
Canned, per 30ml/1 rounded tablespoon	**20**
Creamed, per 28g/1oz	**25**
Fresh or frozen, kernels only, boiled, per 28g/1oz	**25**
Whole baby sweetcorn, canned, drained	**10**
Whole baby sweetcorn, frozen or fresh	**16**

SWEET POTATO

Raw, per 28g/1oz	**26**
Boiled, per 28g/1oz	**24**

SWORDFISH

Fillet, raw, per 28g/1oz	**33**

T

TAHINI

Per 28g/1oz	**170**
Per 15ml/1 level tablespoon	**100**

TAMARILLO

Average fruit, 40g	**18**

TANGERINES

Flesh only, per 28g/1oz	**10**
Flesh with skin, per 28g/1oz	**7**
Whole fruit, 85g/3oz	**20**

TAPIOCA

Per 28g/1oz	**102**

TARAMASALATA
Per 28g/1oz — 135

TARTARE SAUCE
Per 28g/1oz — 80

TAYBERRIES
Per 28g/1oz — 14

TEA
All brands, per cup, no milk or sugar — 0

TIGER NUTS
Per 28g/1oz — 125

TOFU
Per 28g/1oz — 25

TOMATOES
Raw, per 28g/1oz — 4
Canned, per 28g/1oz — 3
Fried, halved, per 28g/1oz — 20
Chutney, per 28g/1oz — 45
Purée, per 28g/1oz — 19
Whole cherry tomato, 21g/³⁄₄oz — 3
Whole medium tomato, 85g/3oz — 12
Per 15ml/1 level tablespoon
Ketchup — 15
Purée — 10

TOMATO JUICE
Per 113ml/4floz — 25

TONGUE
Lamb's, raw, per 28g/1oz — 55
Lamb's, stewed, per 28g/1oz — 82
Ox, boiled, per 28g/1oz — 83

TOPAZ
Flesh only, per 28g/1oz — 16
Flesh and skin, per 28g/1oz — 11
Whole fruit, 170g/6oz — 65

TREACLE
Black, per 28g/1oz — 73
Per 15ml/1 level tablespoon — 50

TRIPE
Dressed, per 28g/1oz — 17
Stewed, per 28g/1oz — 28

TROUT
Fillet, raw, per 28g/1oz — 39
Fillet, smoked, per 28g/1oz — 38
On the bone, poached or steamed, per 28g/1oz — 25
Whole smoked trout, 156g/5½oz — 150
Whole trout, poached or grilled without fat, 283g/10oz raw weight — 250

TUNA
Canned in brine, drained, per 28g/1oz — 30
Canned in oil, per 28g/1oz — 82
Canned in oil, drained, per 28g/1oz — 60
Tuna Steaks, frozen, per 28g/1oz — 32
Tuna Steaks, fresh, raw, per 28g/1oz — 44

TURBOT
Fillet, steamed, per 28g/1oz — 28

TURKEY
Meat only, raw, per 28g/1oz — 30

Meat only, roast, per 28g/1oz — 40
Meat and skin, roast, per 28g/1oz — 48
Turkey ham joint, roast, per 28g/1oz — 35
Turkey ham joint, sliced and grilled, per 28g/1oz — 40
Smoked, meat only, per 28g/1oz — 44

TURNIPS
Raw, per 28g/1oz — 6
Boiled, per 28g/1oz — 4

U

UGLI FRUIT
Flesh only, per 28g/1oz — 15
Flesh and skin, per 28g/1oz — 10
Whole fruit, 397g/14oz — 140

V

VANILLA ESSENCE
Per 28g/1oz — 0

VEAL
Escalope, fried in egg and breadcrumbs, per 28g/1oz — 61
Fillet, raw, per 28g/1oz — 31
Fillet, roast, per 28g/1oz — 65

VENISON
Raw, meat only, per 28g/1oz — 42
Roast, meat only, per 28g/1oz — 56

VINEGAR
Per 28ml/1floz — 1

W

WALNUTS
Shelled, per 28g/1oz — 149
Per walnut half — 15

WATERCHESTNUTS
Canned, per 28g/1oz — 10

WATERCRESS
Per 28g/1oz — 4

WHEAT SPROUTS
Per 28g/1oz — 66

WHEATGERM
Per 28g/1oz — 100
Per 15ml/1 level tablespoon — 18

WHELKS
With shells, boiled, per 28g/1oz — 4
Without shells, boiled, per 28g/1oz — 26

WHITE PUDDING
As sold, per 28g/1oz — 128

WHITEBAIT
Fried, per 28g/1oz — 150

WHITING
Fillet, fried in breadcrumbs, per 28g/1oz — 54
Fillet, raw, per 28g/1oz — 25
Fillet, smoked, raw, per 28g/1oz — 28
Fillet, steamed, per 28g/1oz — 26
On the bone, fried in breadcrumbs, per 28g/1oz — 49
On the bone, steamed, per 28g/1oz — 18

WINKLES
With shells, boiled, per 28g/1oz — 4
Without shells, boiled, per 28g/1oz — 21

WORCESTERSHIRE SAUCE
Per 15ml/1 tablespoon — 13

Y

YAMS
Raw, per 28g/1oz — 37
Boiled, per 28g/1oz — 34

YEAST
Fresh, per 28g/1oz — 15
Dried, per 28g/1oz — 48
Dried, per 5ml/1 level teaspoon — 8

YELLOW BEAN SAUCE
Per 15ml/1 level tablespoon — 20

YOGURT
Low-fat natural, per 28g/1oz — 15
Low-fat natural, per 15ml/1 level tablespoon — 10
Strained, Greek-style, per 28g/1oz — 33
Whole milk, natural, per 28g/1oz — 22

YORKSHIRE PUDDING
Cooked, per 28g/1oz — 60

INDEX

THIN TWIN

Desserts
Apple and Berry Cobbler	87
Banana Fool	82
Bread and Butter Pudding	96
Chilled Lemon Cheesecake	83
Eve's Pudding	87
French Apple Tart	92
Gooseberry Fool	86
Plum Mousse	83
Raspberry Soufflé	82
Rhubarb Chiffon Pie	86
Strawberry Cheesecake	84
Trifle	80

Dips
Blue Cheese	16
Thousand Island	15

Eggs Florentine	47
Eve's Pudding	87

Fish
Baked Crab	24
Haddock Pancakes	74
Halibut Mornay	75
Kedgeree	36
Pie	76
Prawn and Ham Jambayla	75
Prawn Bisque	18
Prawn Cocktail	27
Scallops	26
Smoked Fish Chowder	19
Smoked Salmon Pâté	31
Sole Bonne Femme	74
Spaghetti Alle Vongole	43
Sweetcorn and Crab Soup	23
Tuna Noodle Casserole	42
Tuna Pâté	27
Fish Pie	76
Fish Scallops	26
French Apple Tart	92
French Onion Soup	23

Gooseberry Fool	86

Haddock Pancakes	74
Halibut Mornay	75

Ham, gammon and bacon
Quiche Lorraine	50
Spaghetti Carbonara	44
Spanish Omelet	47
Italian Style Meatballs	67

Ice Cream
Apricot	95
Brown Bread	95
Cherry	94
Strawberry	94

Kedgeree	36

Lamb
Cassoulet	63
Hot Pot	56
Navarin of Lamb	55
Lamb Hot Pot	56
Lasagne	40
Lettuce Soup	22

Macaroni Cheese	48
Moussaka	60

Mousse
Avocado	12
Chicken and Ham	31
Mushroom Pâté	30
Mushroom Soup	22

Navarin of Lamb	55

Passion Cake	90

Pâté
Chicken Liver	30
Country	28
Mushroom	30
Smoked Salmon	31
Tuna	27
Plum Mousse	83

Pork	
Barbecued Pork	59
Cassoulet	63
Chops Normandy	59
Country Pâté	28
Fillet with Prunes	62
Satay	58
Sweet & Sour Pork	58
Pork Chops Normandy	59
Pork Fillet with Prunes	62
Pork Satay	58
Potato Salad	14
Prawn and Ham Jambayla	75
Prawn Bisque	18
Prawn Cocktail	27
Prawns	
Bisque	18
Cocktail	27
Quiche Lorraine	50
Raspberry Soufflé	82
Rendang	55
Rhubarb Chiffon Pie	86
Salad Nicoise	34
Salads	
Coleslaw	14
Potato	14
Salad Nicoise	34
Waldorf Salad	34
Shepherd's Pie	64
Smoked Fish Chowder	19
Smoked Salmon Pâté	31
Sole Bonne Femme	74
Soups	
Cream of Watercress	20
Carrot and Orange	18
Curried Parsnip	26
French Onion	23
Lettuce	22
Mushroom	22
Prawn Bisque	18

Smoked Fish Chowder	19
Sweetcorn and Crab	23
Vichysoisse	19
Spaghetti Alle Vongole	43
Spaghetti Bolognese	42
Spaghetti Carbonara	44
Spanish Chicken	66
Spanish Omelet	47
Strawberry Cheesecake	84
Strawberry Ice Cream	94
Sweet and Sour Pork	58
Sweetcorn and Crab Soup	23
Tagliatelle with Mushrooms	43
Thousand Island Dip	15
Trifle	80
Tuna Noodle Casserole	42
Tuna Pâté	27
Turkey Veronique	66
Vegetable Curry	51
Vegetable Lasagne	50
Vegetables	
Carrot and Orange Soup	18
Coleslaw	14
Cream of Watercress Soup	20
Curried Lentil Rissoles	51
Curried Parsnip Soup	26
Curry	51
French Onion Soup	23
Lasagne	50
Lettuce Soup	22
Mushroom Pâté	30
Mushroom Soup	22
Potato Salad	14
Tagliatelle with Mushrooms	43
Vichysoisse	19
Waldorf Salad	34
Vichysoisse	19
Waldorf Salad	34
Watercress Soup, cream of	20

**THIN
TWIN**

PICTURE CREDITS
Photography:
Steve Lee: pages 13, 17, 21, 49, 53, 61, 69, 73, 97, 89
John Elliott: cover, pages 4, 8
Nick Carmen: page 57
Laurie Evans: page 93
Simon Wheeler: page 81
Illustrations: Claire Attridge